CHRISTIAN FAITH AND
NATURAL SCIENCE

CHRISTIAN FAITH AND NATURAL SCIENCE

KARL HEIM

SCM PRESS LTD
56 BLOOMSBURY STREET
LONDON

The present translation by Neville Horton Smith is based on the first German edition published in 1949 in Tübingen under the title *Der Christliche Gottesglaube und die Naturwissenchaft, I, Grundlegung* by Furche-Verlag. It is the fourth volume of the work by Professor Heim entitled *Der Evangelische Glaube und das Denken der Gegenwart*.

First published in English 1953

Printed in Great Britain by
Northumberland Press Limited
Gateshead on Tyne

PREFACE

THE transformation which is at present taking place in the
natural sciences has evoked a good deal of writing from
Roman Catholic apologists, yet the main school of Protestant
theological thought maintains an attitude of critical aloofness
and declares that the entire discussion is 'out-of-date'. But
if Christianity is not to allow itself to be relegated to the
ghetto, if it is convinced that it has a universal message for the
entire world and that like Paul it is 'a debtor both to the wise
and to the unwise' (i.e. not only to the uneducated but also
to the educated, most of whom today are people with an
education in the natural sciences and technology), then there
is no avoiding discussion between the upholders of the Christian faith and the students of the physical universe. Discussion will be necessary so long as the dichotomy persists between
natural science on the one hand, continually shocking the
world with new discoveries, and on the other hand a living
community, filled like the Apostles with missionary zeal—
'for we cannot but speak the things which we have seen and
heard'.

Discussion between Christianity and the scientifically educated world arises inevitably from this situation, and will
continue, no matter whether it is admitted to the syllabus of
the theological schools or whether it is conducted outside the
boundaries of formal dogmatics. It will continue, no matter
which dogmatic tendency is dominant in theology. It is a
matter of quite irresistible urgency at a time like the present,
when the findings of natural science are raising the most profound philosophical problems, so that every educated person
is directly involved. The present book is nothing more than
a product of this discussion at the point which has now been
reached. It may be that in another twenty years, when
natural science has made further progress, the discussion will

assume a new form. The book will have answered its purpose if it has served at this critical time to give the discussion a new impulse and perhaps to direct it into a new and profitable channel.

KARL HEIM

Tübingen,
   January 1949

CONTENTS

ACKNOWLEDGMENTS

I wɪsʜ to thank my teachers at Bloxham, without whom it would not have been at all possible for me to undertake the translation of a work of this kind; also the Rev. Dr. John Marsh, Professor of Christian Theology in the University of Nottingham, who has given me much-needed encouragement and who has read the proofs; and finally a number of colleagues and friends who have given me useful advice, particularly Mr. Charles Bayes of Cuddesdon College and Dr. C. K. Grant. None of these is at all responsible for any mistranslations of which I may have been guilty.

N. Horton Smith

University of Nottingham
December, 1952

I

INTRODUCTION

1. THE SHOCK ADMINISTERED TO BELIEF BY THE CON-
TEMPORARY PICTURE OF THE PHYSICAL UNIVERSE

In the minds of many thousands of people the period
through which we have been passing has shaken the foundations on which they had built up their belief. It has
confronted them with the ultimate, fundamental question,
whether perhaps it was entirely illusory, this faith of our
forefathers which gave a meaning to human life and to the
whole history of the human race, or whether it is indeed the
case, as the pessimistic author of the Qoheleth puts it, that
'a man hath no pre-eminence above a beast: for all is vanity'
(Eccl. 3. 19ff.). Is there any difference at all between the
wars in which human beings engage in mutual destruction
and the murderous struggles in which the beasts devour one
another? Have not these wars between human beings and
nations the same underlying motives as the conflicts between
beasts and plants: power, the right of the stronger, *Lebens-
raum* and access to the limited sources of nourishment which
this earth affords? Professor Dorn recently worked out an
interesting calculation in order to make clear the significance
which can properly be claimed for the life and history of
mankind in the context of the overall history of the earth.
Let us assume, he says, that the earth is 2,850 million years
old. If we consider this as a day of twenty-four hours, from
midnight to midnight, then the end of the 'stellar age', i.e.
the awakening of organic life on our planet does not occur
until 10.51 p.m., the appearance of man only at twenty-two
seconds before midnight, and the whole of what is called
'world history', including all the establishments of states, the

11

wars between nations, the ideological struggles, the conflicts of the faiths and the foundation of religions, takes place in the last three-tenths of a second. In these circumstances is it not incredibly presumptuous for us human beings to assert that only these last instants in the development of the mammals are 'history' and that everything which preceded them was merely a 'natural process'? That it has been only in these last moments of cosmic time, in which human history has taken place, that the Creator of the universe has come down to earth to speak and to act, and that everything which went before sinks by comparison into insignificance? Does not this assertion of a 'supernatural dignity', raising man above the whole of nature, appear positively grotesque if we consider not merely how short the time is during which mankind has been alive, compared with the thousands of millions of years of the world, but also the infinitesimally small space which human existence occupies in relation to the immeasurable dimensions of the cosmos, as modern astronomy envisages it, and to the cosmic cataclysms of which this immensity is the scene? Our solar system is indeed, as is known, only a part of that lens-shaped cosmic island which is represented by our galaxy, and this has a diameter of about 100,000 light-years (reckoning the velocity of light at 186,282 miles per second). Even within this one galaxy there are estimated to be about 100,000 million light-emitting stars of the same kind as our sun. Yet it is today supposed that this milky way is only one cosmic island amid hundreds of millions of similar islands, some of them combined in still larger systems, the so-called 'clusters', and some visible through our telescopes as spiral nebulae. And now Man, this tiny ephemera, appearing for a few moments on a speck of dust in the cosmos and vanishing again, thinks that he is the crown of creation, the centre around which everything revolves, and that the Creator of all the galaxies has come down to raise him above all the stars!

In the days of the naïve pre-Copernican conception of the universe this religious esteem for man made good sense. The flat, round earth with the starry vault of heaven above it was at that time the cosmic stage on which the whole drama of world events was played out. The sun, the moon, the planets and the stars were the footlights illuminating the play. High above the firmament, above the orbit of Saturn, the most distant of the planets which were known, was the celestial region where God sat enthroned amidst the angels and blessed spirits. God was the invisible Producer and under his direction one act after another of the great universal drama passed over the stage, beginning with the Creation and the Fall and ending with a happy reconciliation. Even Luther, though he knew about the spherical shape of the earth and about the relative size of the sun, still lived in this naïve pre-Copernican world, and so was able to concentrate the whole power of his soul on the central question which was for him the question of all questions: 'How am I to find a merciful God?' He did not need to allow himself to be delayed or diverted from his path by any kind of preliminary question, for within the pre-Copernican universe, according to the opinion of all the philosophers and scientists, it went without saying that the central creature, occupying the centre of the cosmos, was Man, who already on that account stood under the special attention and care of the Lord God reigning in Heaven. It is true that already in Luther's time disquieting lightning-flashes on the distant horizon presaged the coming upheaval which was to snatch away from under Man's feet the firm ground on which he stood in the still centre of the world. Copernicus's work, *De revolutionibus orbium coelestium*, had already appeared, but that did not disturb Luther. He spoke of Copernicus as a new astrologer wanting to prove 'that the Earth is moved and goeth around and not the Sky', which was, he thought, 'the over-witty notion of a Fool, who would fain turn topsy-turvy the whole Art of Astronomy'. He simply points out to him the passage in Joshua which seems to prove indirectly that the sun moves round the earth: 'Sun, stand thou still upon Gibeon; and thou, Moon, in the valley of Ajalon.' Since Luther the situation has fundamentally changed. In his day Man occupied the centre of the cosmos. No one doubted his position as the central creature of the universe. Today Man is an infinitesimal grain of sand in the midst of an immeasurable sandy waste. For this speck of dust to suppose that it is at the centre of the cosmos, and that its eternal future is the main preoccupation of the Creator of the universe, is quite as ridiculous, from the purely scientific point of view, as for a colony of aphides, clustering on the leaf of a tree in the forest, to imagine in a fit of megalomania that not merely the whole leaf but the whole earth exists solely for their sake and that the destruction of the leaf on which they have settled would mean the end of the world. In comparison with the cosmic cataclysms which take place in the circling galaxies, the shattering of our planet in a collision with a comet, which was accepted as probable some forty years ago at the time of the comet scare, or the freezing to death of all the planets of our solar system because of the cooling off of the sun, would be a quite insignificant occurrence. If this entire solar system were to freeze solid with cold or to melt away with heat, that would be as negligible a happening, in relation to the thousands of millions of similar systems which crowd the universe, as when here on earth on some summer evening at the edge of a wood a glow-worm, after rising and gleaming for a few seconds, suddenly loses its light and falls back into the dewy grass.

But it is not only the infinitesimal smallness of our human existence in comparison with the measureless spaces and ages of the cosmos which today confronts every thinking person with the inescapable question, whether it is not a tremendous illusion for us human beings to imagine that the Power which moves the galaxies cares about us. This fundamental question, which involves the ultimate presuppositions on which all religion is based, arises in an almost more direct form at yet another point. This is in that aspect of modern medical science which makes it quite impossible to disregard the complete dependence upon physical events of even the most intimate psychological processes. We need only call to mind some cases which are quite generally known. In the disease usually called 'softening of the brain', which often passes by heredity through several generations, the increasing morbid deterioration of certain parts of the brain induces a mood of depression which in the case of religiously inclined patients takes the form of a morbid conviction which no pastoral exhortation can dispel, the conviction that 'God has rejected me; my fate is sealed; laden with guilt, I am heading for eternal damnation'. Side by side with this there is the opposite and almost more striking case in which a purely physical process does not produce a religious depression but frees the patient from all religious qualms whatsoever. In cases of physiologically conditioned depression, in which the religious responses are often involved, modern medicine applies with great success the electric shock treatment, passing an electric current through leads placed in contact with the patient's temples. These are often people who in their state of depression also despaired of their spiritual salvation, who were a prey in other words to what has been called in theological literature 'certainty of damnation'. And lo and behold! What the minister of religion had tried in vain to achieve with comforting exhortations and encouraging words from the Bible and the Catechism has now been accomplished by the electric current! The depression has gone and the patient not only faces his life with new courage but is filled with a joyful belief in God's forgiveness and in his own eternal salvation. Hundreds of similar examples could be cited, as well as war-time experiences with brain injuries due to head wounds. Injury to a certain part of the brain sometimes resulted in the loss of a whole section of the mental equipment of highly cultured individuals.

Under the impact of all our experiences of this kind we cannot help asking: Everything which goes on in the depths of our souls, and everything with which the theologians are concerned, the consciousness of guilt, remoteness from God, and then again the experience of the nearness of God and of inward peace—is it not all perhaps merely the effect or the reflection of conditions of the brain? Is it not all simply part and parcel of the causal series of physiological processes which it has been possible to influence by the application of a high-frequency electric current? Perhaps even an event so fraught with consequences as Luther's disputation, which gave the decisive impulse to a revolution in the whole history of theology, beginning at the time of the Reformation and continuing in the Lutheran revival of our own day, was no more than the after-effect of a 'trauma' sustained by Luther in his

youth near the village of Stotternheim when lightning struck
the earth very near to him, causing him a shock the effects of
which persisted throughout his life?

2. THE ECLIPSE OF THE RELIGIOUS PROBLEM

In the minds of thousands of our contemporaries all these
fundamental questions, which have here been only lightly
touched upon and recalled to mind, have burst forth again
under the impact of the present universal upheaval with the
force of volcanoes.   But as Helmut Thielicke, in his important and influential essay on 'Secularist Man',[1] quite rightly
points out, these questions are asked only by those who still
stand in some sort of relationship with the belief of the
Church.   The discussion of these questions is not a dialogue
between the Church and the World.   It is never more than a
monologue of the Church with itself.   The word Church must
indeed be taken in a wider sense here than is generally the
case.   The 'Church' in this connotation includes all those
who are still within the field of force of any sort of belief in
supra-sensory realities, whether the belief be Christian, idealistic or anthroposophical in form.   But today there is growing
up to an ever-increasing degree a generation of people who are
separated from any kind of Church by a far deeper gulf than
were the 'atheists' and 'anti-clericals' of earlier times.   The
genuine 'men of the world'—and we came up against them in
barrack rooms and officers' messes far more often in the second
than in the first world war—can be recognized precisely by the
fact that the fundamental questions, which within the *milieu*
of the Church provoke lively discussion—such questions as
'How can God allow it?' or 'Yet God says nothing?'—are no
longer mentioned at all by these true secularists.

But there now arises the question: What lies behind this
silence?   Why does the 'world' with which we have to deal
today no longer ask the question 'Why?' at all, and no longer
wonder what is the meaning of life and what is the meaning
of suffering?   Why is it in consequence completely indifferent

[1] *Der Mensch des Säkularismus*, in *Universitas*, Vol. I, No. 9, and Vol. II,
No. 1.

to all the endeavours of the Church's apologists to bring the belief of the Church into harmony with the modern conception of the physical universe? Kurt Ihlenfeld attempts to explain this silence by saying that modern man stands unquestioningly in the darkness of the world because the darkness is after all impenetrable. He accepts the darkness as darkness and maintains an attitude of resignation. But if someone feels that the 'horizons are lost in impenetrable gloom' and that it is better not to gaze into the void, for if he does the void may gaze into him (Nietzsche), he has still not ceased to ask what is the meaning of human existence. He has merely found no answer to these questions, and he does not expect an answer from anyone else, least of all from a religious apologist. That is why his attitude to all these problems is persistently one of shoulder-shrugging resignation. A person in this condition is still obsessed with these questions as a repressed complex or as the remains of an outworn religious tradition. That is still not genuine secularism, such as one finds for example in large sections of the American population which are no longer attached to any Church. On the contrary, it is characteristic of the genuine secularist that world events do not seem in the least obscure and problematic to him, but perfectly clear and intelligible. The apparent obscurity is only present, he thinks, so long as one continues to live in the dream world from which the religious person cannot escape; it vanishes when one returns to the firm ground of reality. The nature of genuine secularism becomes plain to us if we pass in review, for example, the characters in Ernst Wiechert's new novel, *The Jeromin Children,* in which the destiny of our time is especially clearly mirrored. These characters in a way represent a progression, extending from passionate atheism, still contending with Providence and asking questions of the Church, through to that clear and serene secularism, in which all these questionings and accusations against the divine government of the world are no longer uttered at all. On the lowest plane was parson Agricola, who had taken to drink 'because he had stopped believing in God'. His housemaid had run away 'because he spent the whole night drinking and cursing God'. His condition came to a

B

head in the most terrible outburst when an epidemic had broken out in his village and the neighbouring ones, and a large number of children had died. 'Come here, you child-killer!' he shouted. 'Show me the blood on your hands! Put them here! Closer! So that I can dry them for you! You weren't satisfied, were you, with the firstborn in Egypt or the innocents at Bethlehem? Not even your own Son was enough for you. You nailed Him to the Cross to redeem us. . . . But you still wanted these children—seventy-one of them in ten villages!' . . . And he shook his fist at the crucifix and hurled his glass of red wine against the wall, so that it dripped from the bright wallpaper like blood. 'God could help, but He does not exist. Thinking kills God, and He has put into our hands the means of His own death. He would like to take it back, but it is too late; we will not give it up again.' This condition, in which a man accuses a person who, as he himself says, does not exist at all, and thus cannot merit any reproaches, is only the first phase of secularism, a state of fermentation, in which the wine is still new and is therefore not yet clear. People who have formerly held the old view of the nature of the universe find themselves first of all in this initial stage of secularism, which is exhibited in a quite over-whelming form in a number of characters in the books of E. E. Dwinger. On a rather higher level than Agricola there is the aristocratic Herr von Balk, who with cool self-assurance mocks at God, the world and life, with its 'cruelty', its arbitrariness and its complete meaninglessness. 'Life today is just as bloody and as sordid as it was ten thousand years ago and in another ten thousand years it will be no different.' He protests against the way in which 'the deep inarticulate anxiety of every creature has had presented to it the coloured pictures of a magic lantern, the magic consolations of the millennia, of which the ultimate goal was nothing other than a blissful hereafter, as blissful as the passage through the present world was accursed'. Yet amid this cynical mocking, like a gleam of light in the darkened consciousness of an inebriate, there arises the feeling that there exists a higher form of secularism, in which there is no more mocking or protesting: 'no ill-feeling, you understand? One must live without any ill-feeling. That is what matters.' Yet only one person in the novel has really achieved this aim. That is Jumbo, the most significant and impressive character in the book; the man under whose influence Jons Ehrenreich Jeromin, the central figure of the novel, began to move in the direction which led him to the goal. The secularism which is embodied in Jumbo has become free of any ill-feeling and of any complaining against fate. Modestly and unpretentiously the man takes his proper place in the unchanging order of the world and the eternal laws of existence. The practical attitude which is possible for a man, all of whose religious cloud-pictures have lost their definition, is to help and love his fellow human beings with the purpose of easing the inevitable pains of the struggle for existence which is ordained for us, at least so far as this can be done by the means available to modern medicine. 'Those people,' thought Jumbo, 'who say that one day someone is going to wipe away their tears— they know nothing. They were not modest enough. They were not children of earth; they wanted Paradise. Do not aim at Paradise. Do not pick a quarrel with God, but tighten your chin-strap when you see that he is gunning for you.' The man who has reached this state does not utter a single word of resentment against the arbitrariness and meaningless-ness of what goes on in the world, for he has realized that all these complaints against our destiny arose from the old naïve conception of the universe, the blue dome of heaven rising above the terrestrial stage on which the cosmic drama was performed, with Man in the leading rôle, his story beginning in the Garden of Eden and ending in eternal bliss in a future Paradise. So long as the small human flock was at the centre of universal history, Man was in a position to establish claims. Providence had to take notice of him. He could demand that his life should have a meaning, and that ultimately, through striving and death, he should reach the goal that was set before him. He could ask what was the reason, if the course of world events did not satisfy his aspirations. With the collapse of this naïve conception of the universe, since the earth which mankind inhabits had become a mere dot amid the immensity of the galaxies, this claim of Man, together with all complaints against the ordering of the world and all questionings about the reason for it, lost its meaning.

This attitude of the serene secularist is very movingly expressed in the quiet, unassuming way in which Jumbo dies on the field of battle in Russia. In the midst of the boundless snows of the Russian steppes, cut off from their unit, two men are lying, like imperceptible dots in the cosmic immensity. They are Jumbo and the 'little lieutenant'. Both have stomach wounds. With tremendous difficulty and using up the last of his strength, Jumbo does his friend a final good turn. He hands him the rum-flask and speaks to him re-assuringly. 'Don't you think anyone will come?' asked the lieutenant. 'No, there's no one coming. We've had it, old man, and it's time for us to forget our pettifogging earthly ill-feelings.' Jumbo drank the rest of the rum and let the flask fall. '*Exitus letalis,*' he murmured, 'that's what the big medical men call it. . . . It has not been so bad as they always made out.' He fell asleep quite quietly, with no pain. His eyes closed of their own accord. With his last, weary glance he saw the silver stars high above, looking as though they were embroidered on the black tester over a four-poster bed. Thus he died; it was like the extinguishing of a solitary candle in the midst of the radiant cosmic night in which stars and solar systems move in their courses according to eternal laws. Not until six months later were the bodies of the two missing men dug out from the melting snow.

In the state of mature and serene secularism, which is so movingly exemplified in this simple, unpretentious way of dying, two courses of action are open to us. The first consists in taking our place quietly and unassumingly in the order to which the whole of world events is subject; in aspiring only to be 'children of earth', to live like those 'who tilled the soil and looked no farther . . . who cherished no ambition, engaged in no speculation, were without dreams and without philosophy, who went on ploughing just as man had first ploughed outside the gates of Paradise, and who will continue to plough, whether the gates of Paradise be opened or whether the prospect of Paradise be lost for ever'. The second course of action open to us, when we have shaken off all our metaphysical dreams and found our way back to earth, is that which Jons followed when he had finished chasing after the chimera of the universal reformers. He came home to his native countryside, to live there as panel doctor for a dozen villages, instead of devoting his life to the entire world.

The impression made upon us by this serene secularism in which a man like Jumbo lived and died may perhaps make clearer to us than any theoretical consideration of the essential characteristics of the secularist outlook why it is that in the minds of thousands of our contemporaries religious problems, including the questions of the reason for our existence and of the meaning of life, are no longer raised. It is certainly hardly true to say that this is due to the 'dropping of the question of truth'. On the contrary, the mature secularist lives in the conviction that he alone has returned to the solid ground of reality and that the rest of us are still pursuing chimeras which have long since lost their significance. Nor does the genuine secularist feel that the horizon of his life is shrouded in obscurity. He feels rather as though a fresh morning breeze had cleared away the vapours which had risen from the river and veiled the hills and forests in grey mist. Now the land-scape is suddenly filled with light and the outlines become clear and distinct. There comes into being a new, self-contained, comprehensive conception of reality. We perceive that the cosmic stream of events, however extravagant the multiplicity of forms it comprises and however astonishing the wealth of varying shapes which it produces, is still ultimately subject to a single universal fundamental law. Whether we compute in terms of thousands of millions of years the times in which the galaxies turn in their orbits; or whether we calculate the movements of the electrons around the nucleus of the atom; or observe the avalanche, set in motion by a shot from a sporting gun and hurtling down to the valley, engulfing the huts and cottages in its path; or contemplate the silent warfare which is being fought out in the vegetable kingdom, in the primeval forest where monstrous parasitic plants entwine the gigantic trees until their fatal embrace brings them to a lingering death; or watch the tiny caterpillars, the offspring of the 'nun moth', which produces them by the million in a very short time, crawl up the trunks of the pine-trees and devour the pine-needles, so that soon for miles on end all that is left is a bald, dead, ghost forest; or share in the dismay which is felt when a single sharp frosty night in May destroys all the fruit blossom of a season; or look pityingly at an entire anthill, with all its ingenious constructions, the result of untiring and minute labour, crushed in an instant by the hoof of a passing ox; or whether we feel a certain sympathy for the millions of flies which in the course of a hot summer, despite desperate efforts to free themselves, die miserably on the sticky fly-papers which Man has put there to destroy them; or whether we share in the experience of the world wars in which the nations of mankind engage together, wars in which whole states, together with their entire cultural heritage, despite the most desperate defence, succumb to the superior might of a more powerful coalition—all these are after all nothing more than variations on a single theme, on which the changes are rung but which keeps returning despite all the multiplicity of shapes and forms. Everywhere in the world, in the realm of astronomical figures and in the narrowest domain of the protons and electrons, in the fields of physics and biology and in inorganic and organic nature, everywhere we find the same play of forces. The weaker gives way to the stronger, even though it may first have offered a prolonged and determined resistance. It has always been so and it will always be so. This primary law is obeyed throughout all spaces and throughout all times.

That is the clear, perspicuous, overall picture of reality on the basis of which the genuine secularist conducts his life and thinking. And it is upon this fundamental law that his interpretation of all religions and his entire ethic are based. If this fundamental rule is everywhere dominant, then religious convictions can obviously never be anything else than a 'reflection of the *bios* basis' (Thielicke). All representations of gods are symbolic images with a power of suggestion, and both in the individual matching of strength and in the collective national struggle for existence they instil new strength into the combatants. A god who performs this service must obviously not be a 'god opposed to mankind'; he must give his blessing to the weapons of those who are engaged in the battle. 'Providence' is a means of mass suggestion, imparting a religious prestige to the decisions of those who wield 'the power. All this does not mean, as it seems to do from the standpoint of the Christian, that God is reduced to the rôle of a servant of Man who is in rebellion against him. This is rather the only form in which the secularist overall view of reality permits religion to retain a positive significance. The ethic which is founded on this conception of the universe cannot be anything other than a thoroughgoing pragmatism, an instrument to serve in the struggle for power which is the sole purpose of all activity in the world. 'Good' is what is useful to me in the individual and collective struggle for power and what furnishes me with the strength to maintain my position in this struggle.

From the simple, self-contained world-picture of thoroughgoing secularism there quite logically results for people with combative characters that attitude which was most impressively exemplified by Ernst Jünger in his earlier period. The meaning of life is not to be found in the achievement of an ideal of any kind or in the championing of any sort of partisan doctrine, but simply in the struggle itself, in the total mobilization, the total placing on a war footing of the whole human personality. This new and more daring way of living, in which all doctrines and philosophies lose their relevance, was then, according to Rauschning's analysis,[1] put into practice in the 'nihilist revolution' by the '*élite*' which was assembled and led by Hitler. This '*élite*' sees the meaning of life in living dangerously, its task in ruling, the means to its end in violence, and its ultimate goal in all-embracing, total domination over the world. All ideas, even the idea of nationalism, are mere 'stage properties', mere tricks of the trade and suggestive catchwords to transform the masses into a tractable instrument to assist the '*élite*' in its rise to power.

That, in brief outline, is the essential attitude of mature secularism, which is, indeed, convinced that it is firmly based

---

[1] Hermann Rauschning, *Die Revolution des Nihilismus*, Europa-Verlag, Zurich and New York. Translated by E. W. Dickes under the title *Germany's Revolution of Destruction*, Heinemann, London, 1939.

on the unshakable foundation of the modern scientific conception of the universe and especially on that which follows from the conclusions of astronomy, physics and biology.

We have no right to raise a passionate protest against the re-interpretation of all religious and ethical fundamental concepts which secularism is undertaking and to oppose it as a rebellion against God and a human self-deification, so long as we are not in a position to propose, as an alternative to the overall view of reality from which this re-interpretation necessarily follows, another conception of the universe and one in which nature and man appear in a different light.

3. THE BASIS FOR DISCUSSION OF THE CONTEMPORARY
   PICTURE OF THE PHYSICAL UNIVERSE

Everything which has been said so far has shown that the genuine secularism with which we are confronted to-day is neither a Promethean rebellion of mankind against God nor the expression of a weary resignedness in the face of the darkness which enshrouds our existence. It is rather the necessary consequence of a conception of the universe which, precisely because of its simplicity and perspicuity and its elimination of all kinds of obscure, metaphysical, cosmic substrata, presents itself with the force of evidence to the people of the machine age who have lived through two world wars. We are living in a time when in all civilized countries the tide of secularism is slowly but continually rising and the proportion of people still attached to any kind of church even in the Anglo-Saxon countries is steadily diminishing. Amid this rising flood of secularism there floats the ark of the Church. The Church is like a ship on whose deck festivities are still kept up and glorious music is heard, while deep below the water-line a leak has been sprung and masses of water are pouring in, so that the vessel is settling hourly lower though the pumps are manned day and night.

The loss of interest in the religious question is indeed the tacit expression of a very radical problem, a problem which is far more radical than all those questions of detail which used, in the days of the older school of apologetics, to arouse such lively discussions between the Church and her opponents. The fundamental question which is now to be debated is not concerned with any one single point in the Church's teaching. It is concerned with the whole. It is the question whether for people of the present time, whose thought is shaped by the contemporary conception of the physical universe, any other philosophy is still possible than that of secularism. Does not any other outlook imply a relapse into the world-picture of our fathers which has long since been rendered obsolete by scientific research and the experience of everyday life? But the fundamental question which confronts us here is not merely put to the Church from outside, by the 'world'. No, there are also thousands of people living within the *milieu* of the Church who are to-day oppressed by this radical problem. We know from our own experience that every stunning blow dealt us by fate, which inwardly quite throws us off our balance and shatters everything which gave our life a mean-ing, forces upon us the grave temptation which lies in asking whether perhaps it is really as the world says, whether per-haps everything is merely a blind interplay of forces, in which at all times the lesser power, despite all the resistance it offers, is relentlessly crushed by the greater. Has it not always been so and will it not be so always? In such hours of temptation we become aware that the advancing tide of secularism does not merely rage around us from without. It rather traverses our own hearts. As soon as some great blow makes us abandon even for a single moment the foothold on belief which had kept us above water, we inevitably hurtle down into the dark gulf and are swept away by the secularist flood. The secularist world-picture, which is nowadays everywhere in the air, en-folds us with its subtle enchantment and its power to force intellectual acceptance. And so the dialogue between the Church and the world is in truth transformed into a mono-logue which is carried on within the *milieu* of the Church herself, and indeed within the ambit of our own troubled and tempted hearts.

We cannot, then, escape the challenge of the overall con-ception of reality which the 'world' substitutes for the philo-sophy of belief, even if we remain entirely within the *milieu* of the Church. We are now no longer free to ask whether we should accept this challenge at all, or whether this discussion with secularism should be suspended in view of certain theological objections. This question has lost its relevance, for we are all already involved in this discussion in every hour of temptation. The only question which can be asked now is *how* the discussion is to be conducted and what is to be the starting-point for the debate. The answer follows necessarily from the circumstances in which we find ourselves. We are confronted with an overall picture of reality which is imposingly comprehensive and coherent. We can counter this overall conception only by proposing a different overall conception which, just like the world-picture of secularism, comprises the entire reality of the universe as we see it to-day, from the spiral nebulae down to the electrons.

The history of Protestantism took an unhappy turn when, soon after the time of Schleiermacher, Protestant theology severed its connexion with philosophy in order to become an independent field of science. Since then it has shown more and more reluctance to undertake the difficult task of opposing the world-picture of disbelief with a world-picture of belief. It has been content to extract from the overall picture of reality, which the believer as well as the unbeliever must always have in his mind if he is to be a responsible agent in the affairs of this world, the central theme, the history of our salvation, which tells how mankind, created by God, falls and is redeemed and perfected, and to develop this central theme in every direction. It thought it could quite confidently leave all the rest to the profane sciences. In the Reformation period and the ensuing centuries this restriction of theological study to a single section of reality as a whole was perfectly feasible, for at that time the remaining part of the world-picture, the part with which the profane sciences were concerned, was simply a further development of the central content of the faith, which was the subject-matter of theology. The close and intimate correspondence which existed between the theological centre and the peripheral parts of the overall world-picture found its expression in the fact that within the university theology occupied the central position as 'queen of the sciences'. The whole body of the profane sciences, especially philosophy and natural science, was merely the *ancilla theologiae*, the handmaiden of theology.

To-day the situation is completely changed. Amid the totally transformed environment of the modern academic disciplines, the basic assumptions of which have entirely altered, if the confession of faith of the Reformers is stated at all nowadays it makes the same impression as would a last-remaining venerable fragment of wall, all that is left standing of a medieval cathedral in a half-destroyed town, appearing as a foreign body amidst the newly erected blocks of offices and flats of a modern city. During the last war a deep impression was made when, after an air raid on Mayence, all that remained standing of a church dedicated to St. John the Baptist was a fragment of a doorway on which were inscribed the words: 'Repent ye: for the kingdom of heaven is at hand!' But this ruin from the past could not be left standing like that permanently. Either it could be built up again into a complete church of a design which fitted in with it, or it would have to be pulled down and cleared away. In a present-day university, with its research institutes and clinics, the theology of the Reformation makes a similar impression. Either this ruin from the past must be cleared away—that is to say there is no room left for theology in a present-day university—or else this fragment left over from another conception of reality must be built up again and completed so that it forms a comprehensive world-picture. Unless this is done, it has become meaningless. Only when the whole is again visible, of which this fragment forms a part, will it be possible to discuss it seriously. But the question here is not the relatively unimportant one of the position of theology in the structure of the present-day universities. Something far more important is at stake, namely the credibility of the Christian message in the world of today.

Everyone today knows from experience that all responsible speech and action rests upon an overall picture of reality. It is only on the basis of this comprehensive view of the whole that we can make decisions in any specific matter, for it is only then that we see all the possibilities which are latent in this whole, in which, after all, all the single parts interact. Any medical prescription, for example, rests upon the completeness of the view of reality which the doctor has gained from his diagnosis and from his knowledge of the medicines which are available to us on the basis of modern natural science. If any important factor has been left out of consideration, this mistaken diagnosis may cost a human life. The same is true of any responsible decisions taken by a statesman. These too depend upon a complete and comprehensive picture of the relative distribution of power within the modern world and of the technical means of waging war which our present knowledge of nature places at our disposal. We have confidence in a doctor or a statesman only when we are convinced that he really exactly observes and thoroughly understands the overall situation and that he is making his decision conscientiously and on the basis of the fullest possible knowledge. It is only then that we can entrust ourselves to his leadership. But if it happens that someone seizes power who is himself uncertain about the real situation in the world as a whole because he lacks the necessary expert knowledge, then we cannot have confidence in him. He is an irresponsible gambler and his gambling may bring whole nations to perdition. The fanaticism which informs his speaking and with which he endeavours from the very outset to override and shout down the doubts and questions raised by his hearers is in itself a sign of inward uncertainty and a symptom of the condition of morbid convulsion which determines his actions.

A similar impression is made on the people of today by a Church which on the one hand exhorts them in forceful terms to have faith and to be loyal to their religion, and on the other hand leaves those who would like to entrust themselves to its leadership entirely in the dark with regard to the overall picture of reality of which the proposed religious belief must be an integral part. The reasons which impel the Church to avoid a discussion of the general conception of reality have certainly, within the *milieu* of the Church, a certain justification. It is said, for example, that it is not at all the business of the Church to answer the question which the 'world', on the basis of its own view of nature, puts to her. Discussions of this

kind, opposing belief and history or belief and science, belong
to the period of the older school of apologetics which has now
long since been superseded. They can only lead to a new
'natural theology', and we must not relapse into that. We
human beings have no right at all to ask God questions; it is
for God to ask questions and to call us to account. These considerations no doubt afford a certain sense of relief for the
believing member of the Church. When he is told this, he
has the reassuring feeling that it is no longer necessary for him
at all, as a present-day Christian, to concern himself with the
fundamental doubts and questions which were a serious
stumbling-block for earlier generations and which he too has
already often enough found troublesome. But these considerations make a completely different impression on the
other people, on those who are outside the Church's ambit.
The reasons by which the Church asserts her right to refuse
to give any answer to the radical question, with which secularism confronts us by the mere fact of its existence, do not make
upon the secularist the impression of unshakable religious
conviction which they are intended to make. The Church's
attitude here tends rather to make the outsider suspect that
she is perhaps herself not quite certain about the truth of her
profession and that this is the reason why she refuses to provide any detailed information about the philosophical basis on
which she stands. The Church's future today depends more
than ever on whether she withdraws into the ghetto and leaves
the world to its fate, or whether she has the authority to continue the discussion with the world outside and to answer the
questions which it puts to her. We cannot today, even within
the *milieu* of the Church, simply presuppose the existence of
God as axiomatic and reject from the outset the greatest question of all, the question whether God is, or whether the overwhelming majority of our contemporaries are right in
regarding God as merely 'an attitude' and not as a foundation,
as merely a 'doubtful possibility', which may perhaps still just
keep our heads above water, as Christoph Schrempf[1] once said.
At a time when this question is not merely being asked outside

[1] The first translator of Kierkegaard's works into German. He later abandoned Christian belief.

the Church, but may again and again arise even in our own hearts, it seems to betray an unhealthy and over-tense attitude, a sign of inward uncertainty, if we simply attempt to banish this whole problem to the realm of the subconscious mind. As soon as we raise the question at all, and abandon our violent endeavours to repress it, we can no longer limit the range of our considerations to a single section of reality as a whole, for example, to the history of the salvation of mankind. For if God exists, then our gaze must be directed to the whole of the universe with all that it comprises. For God is the omnipresent Creator and Lord, who controls the rotation of the galaxies just as He controls the circling of the electrons within the atom.

The attempt to reject out of hand the fundamental question, the question which concerns the whole, does not merely run counter to the Church's 'readiness to come out into the open'; it also brings with it a grave danger for our own personal lives. For in the last analysis it is an effort to overcome the dictates of conscience and a rebellion against God, who has placed us in a reality which inevitably confronts us with questions of this kind and who has given us an intelligence which cannot rest until we have sought for some sort of answer to these questions. The attempt to avoid an honest discussion of these questions may lead to grave consequences at some point in our lives. It may bring about a sudden disaster if these questions arise again under the impact of some great trouble which befalls us. The campanile in St. Mark's Square in Venice collapsed in broad daylight. No one understood at first how that could have happened. The building material had been good and the structure was architecturally perfectly sound. There was only one reason for the disaster. Some of the wooden piles in the foundations, on which the ancient bell-tower had been erected centuries earlier in the lagoon, had become rotten and were no longer able to carry the weight of the building. One may say that any fundamental question with which we have not come to grips is a rotten beam which forms part of the underlying structure of our philosophy of life. A dogmatic system may be comprehensive and coherent, inspired with a reforming spirit and constructed in the imposing style of the dialectical method. The building material is good and the structure is architecturally sound. But there is still a rotten beam incorporated in the unseen foundations. The fundamental questions have been disregarded, with which reality in the light of the contemporary conception of the physical universe confronts us. In an hour of temptation this rotten beam may bring about the collapse of the whole proud edifice overnight.

Because that is so, the theme with which we are going to deal in the following sections is not, as many people suppose, a purely peripheral problem having nothing to do with the central problems of belief and consequently of possible interest only for those whose special hobby is out-of-the-way subsidiary questions of this kind. The matter with which we are concerned here is not something which lies on the periphery but a part of the foundations. We are concerned with a preliminary question, not with the central question of belief. But this preliminary question is a fundamental one, because the entire edifice is in danger of collapse if it remains unanswered. The whole dispute in which religions, Churches, denominations and theological tendencies have been engaged with one another for centuries loses its relevance from the outset and nothing whatever is to be gained by devoting one's enthusiasm to it so long as no answer has been given to the question whether the whole thing is not after all, as Feuerbach supposed, only a projection of human requirements on to the clouds or merely thought-formations which emanate from the individual or collective subconscious of puny human beings.

We can see from all this that, however imperfect and provisional the answer may be which can be given in a book like this to the fundamental questions with which we are here confronted, we must still not repress these questions. We must face them squarely and go into them thoroughly. For what is at stake is the significance and justifiability of all religious seeking and striving. How are we to set about this investigation? Where are we to start? When we approach these problems in the following sections, the method which first suggests itself is that which is commonly followed even today in countless minor works of apologetics in coming to terms

with natural science. One begins by allowing the scientist
to say his piece and then on the basis of his report one envisages the conception of reality which is valid according to the
latest state of scientific research. After that one asks whether
belief in a Creator is still compatible with this contemporary
scientific view of the universe. In view of this modern world-
picture is it still possible to cling to a belief in a God who
works miracles and grants prayers? Can belief in the Bible
be defended against the objections which arise out of this
conception of the physical universe? But thankful as we are
that at this very time, according to the testimony of such leading scientists as Max Planck, natural science has entered a
phase which Bavink was able to describe under the heading,
'Science on the Road to Religion', we still have from the
outset, in dealing with this method of apologetic, the feeling
that it brings us into a position of complete dependence on
the momentary phase in which scientific research happens to
be. We are 'playing the market'. We are making use of the
favourable wind which is coming to us for the moment if not
by any means from all then at least from some of the acknowledged leaders of scientific research; we are trimming our sail
to catch this wind, so that it may drive the ship of the Church
forward upon her course. But this dependence upon the passing phase of natural science might immediately become
dangerous if the wind were to veer round and if belief were
once again compelled to ply to windward.

We need a firm basis which will render us independent of
momentary currents of scientific opinion. We can attain such
a basis only if there is something which lies from the outset
outside the whole scope of natural science, some position
which is entirely beyond the range of the scientific method, a
firm point which cannot be subjected to the spatial and temporal measurements with which natural science works, and
which lies even beyond the incalculable dimensions of the
cosmos in comparison with which Man sinks into nothingness.
We need a position which does not have to be defended against
scientific objections, a position from which, if the necessity
should arise, we could go over from the defensive to the attack
in our relations with natural science. Does any such impreg-

nable stronghold exist, which can serve us as a base of operations in undertaking a thoroughgoing settlement of accounts with the ultimate presuppositions of the scientific method? Or is it not true that everything which forms part of reality is drawn in by virtue of that fact alone into the sphere of exact scientific observation and analysis? That is the question on which everything depends. Only if some such unassailable position exists can we come to grips with the questions with which we are here confronted. In the following sections we wish, therefore, to follow a course which is the opposite of that followed in traditional apologetics. We do not start out from the conclusions of natural science but begin by constructing a philosophical basis. We set about this task in Section I by speaking of a reality which is beyond the reach of scientific investigation. This first reality is our own ego, the active subject in the whole process of scientific knowing, whose existence must be presupposed if natural science is to be 'possible in the first place'. Only after that do we intend to speak in a subsequent section of the second reality, one which cannot like the first be taken for granted but which must nevertheless be discussed before we can begin to come to terms with natural science. This second reality is God. The existence of God cannot be taken for granted. It is possible to deny the existence of God. But the question whether God exists or does not exist is not amenable to the scientific method. It cannot be decided by observation or experiment. Nevertheless, even though it lies outside the range of his scientific work, the natural scientist too cannot simply leave the question of the existence or non-existence of God open and adopt a neutral attitude towards it. Even in his scientific research the first starting-point and the ultimate goal must be either the denial or the acceptance of God. It is not our intention here to assert dogmatically, as is done in a theological treatise, that the reality of God occupies this position of unique significance. If we were to do so, everything which is built up on this assumption would be acceptable only for the small circle of those who, by virtue of their experience of life or of their membership of a church, are subject to the authority which can utter the all-powerful phrase: *Deus dixit,* God hath

c

spoken. Our present intention, in accordance with the special purpose of the book, is to demonstrate in a form which is intelligible to any thinking person that not only the ego but also the reality of the personal God in fact belongs to a dimension which is different from those of everything which is accessible to scientific investigation. From this there will follow a demonstration of the insuperable barrier which modern science encounters whenever it approaches the ultimate problem. We shall thus have attained the vantage-points from which, in Part II, we shall undertake our consideration of modern natural science, the principal conclusions of physics and biology, and the position which Man occupies within the contemporary conception of nature. The two parts together are to serve as a basis for the third, which is to present a comprehensive and coherent picture of the creation and perfecting of the world in the light of scientific research and the biblical outlook.

II

THE EGO AND THE WORLD

4. THE ENIGMA OF OUR PERSONAL EXISTENCE

For all of us, including those of us who approach the problem from the other point of departure, that from which the natural scientist sets out on the road of inductive observation, coming always nearer to the supreme goal but never able to attain it, the first, immediate datum is not the contents of our sense perceptions and of the measurements deduced from them. The dome of glittering stars above us which affords us an idea of the galactic systems ranging over hundreds of thousands of light-years, the electric waves which vibrate through the molecular world of the atoms, the miracle of life evolving upwards before our eyes within a span of some fifteen hundred million years from the original plant to man—all this is not the first datum. What is closest and most intimately known to all of us, what we find when we try to look around ourselves in the world, is, as it were, the belvedere on which we stand when we wish to survey the immense panorama of nature, the observatory from which all this reveals itself to us. For each of us it is his own ego, which stands closer than the whole objective universe, is constantly bombarded by this entire plenitude of overwhelming impressions, and must somehow inwardly come to grips with it all and master it. The world of nature, which is experienced, measured and computed from this point of vantage, is always only the second datum. The first is the primary reality which Fichte has in mind in the introduction to the *Theory of Science* when he says: 'Look at yourself. Turn your gaze away from all that surrounds you and towards your own inward self. That is the first demand which philosophy makes of its

35

pupil. Nothing outside you matters here, but only you yourself.'

We must revert in this connexion to what was necessarily said in the first volume of this work[1] about the ego and develop a little further the argument which was propounded there. For it will subsequently become clear that at this very time natural science is being faced in quite a new way with the fact that we can always see reality only from this central viewpoint. The odd thing about the ego, which takes the world of nature as the object of its perception and volition, is that although it is nearest and most familiar to us, and although each of us is immediately aware of it, yet it is downright impossible for us to describe it objectively, as we can describe a crystal or a flower or a house. As Heinrich Rickert puts it, in his book *The Object of Knowledge,*[2] 'I am not the body which I call my body. This bodily organism is indeed the object of my knowledge and the instrument of my will, but it is not my ego. Nor am I the world of my consciousness, the wealth of visual images, auditory and tactile sensations, thoughts, memories, dreams, joys, pains, volitional impulses, emotions and passions which flood through my soul in an unending stream. It is true that all these contents of consciousness pass before me like a column of troops marching past their commander at a review or like a flock of migratory birds which I watch from my window. But I myself, the invisible spectator, am not a part of the contents of my consciousness. That is already implied in the fundamental optical fact that the seeing point is itself not visible; as soon as a point becomes visible, it is no longer the seeing point. In order to see something, for example the letters in a book lying in front of me, I must keep it at least a short distance away from me. So I can never see myself, because I can never confront myself with myself.' At first it seems to follow from this that there is nothing at all which we can say about ourselves. It seems as though, to borrow Fritz Künkel's expression, one can speak of the subject only 'nonically', i.e. by denying all relations. But strangely enough that

[1] *Glaube und Denken (Belief and Thought),* 4 III and IV, pages 84ff.
[2] *Der Gegenstand der Erkenntnis.*

is not the case. On the contrary. I can make much more
definite statements about myself than about anything which
confronts me as an object. These are the so-called existential
propositions which Heidegger distinguishes from the categories in which we frame objective experiences. I know, of
course, that everything I assert about myself existentially is
expressed figuratively, for language must always employ
optical images; but we are speaking here of something which
cannot be optically perceived. I know, too, that everything I
say about myself in this figurative form is intended to convey
something quite definite which everyone else to whom I talk
about it understands at once without my giving him proofs
of it, because he knows just as well about himself as I know
about myself.

The first existential proposition which I must assert about
myself is this: I stand with respect to certain quite definite,
concrete and clearly distinguishable and circumscribable contents of the objective world of experience in the relation
which we express with the word 'my'. I say this is 'my'
body and not your body or someone else's body. I speak of
'my' consciousness, 'my' thoughts and recollections, 'my'
dreams, 'my' volition, activity and passivity, 'my' destiny and
'my' death, distinguishing these from the corresponding
experiences of everyone else. It is not death in general that I
am heading for. 'My' death is coming to me. I have seen a
hundred other people die; but now it is my own turn. A well-
known German scholar was visited during his last illness by a
colleague who tried to console him by saying: 'Modern
medicine can make dying extraordinarily easy for us with
pain-killing injections.' Whereupon he raised himself from
his pillow with a last effort and said: 'Nobody shall deprive
me of *my* death.' In all these contexts the word 'my' has a
quite special meaning. We do not use it to denote a relation
of *ownership*. It may be that my body no longer belongs to
me. I may be the bondservant of another. Nor is it certain
that I am the master of the contents of my consciousness. I
may suffer from inescapable delusions which pursue me day
and night. I cannot even bring about my death myself; the
decision lies in the hands of others. It may be that even my

will is not under my control. I may no longer possess a will of
my own. The dæmonic will of another may have supplanted
it. All this does not make the slightest difference to the fact
that, in this special sense, I call the body, the range of thoughts
and the will which are no longer under my control 'my' body,
'my' consciousness and 'my' will. This does not denote the
local relationship we have in mind when we say: 'The flat I
occupy is my home, the place where I live; the workshop
where I am employed is my place of work, the place where I
am to be found during working hours.' It is true that if we
want to speak graphically there is indeed no better illustration
for the mysterious relationship in which I stand with regard
to 'my' body than the spatial relationship between two objects
one of which contains the other. We are inclined to say: 'My
soul is in my body just as the kernel is in the nutshell or
the bird in the cage.' And this shows that the body appears to
us as the dwelling-house, the inn or sometimes the prison of
the soul; the soul may quit it when the moment of liberation
comes of which Hölderlin is thinking when he writes:

> In the most glorious of tempests
> May the wall of my prison fall in ruin.
> More glorious and more free
> May my spirit go forth into the unknown land.

Yet precisely this comparison, which immediately suggests
itself, with the relationship in space between two objects, one
of which contains the other, is in fact a quite particularly mis-
leading one, because it always brings us back into the myth-
ology of primitive animism. If we wish to achieve a correct
understanding of what is meant by 'being mine', we must
free ourselves entirely from this notion of a local relation. I
myself am neither in my body nor above it nor beside it. I am
on this side of all objectivity, and consequently outside all
three-dimensional space. The relation which here comes into
force, which Heidegger has called 'each-mine-ness' (*Jemeinig-
keit*), is absolutely opposed to all objective relations and
presents no analogy whatever with any of them.

That I stand in this unparalleled relationship to a certain

section of the world of objects is, however, not the only existential proposition which I must assert about myself. The second proposition is this: I cannot substitute another content for the content to which I stand in this relation. I am bound to it by a fatal necessity. Heidegger says that existence (*Dasein*, literally 'being *there*') is 'being cast into one's *there*' or 'being delivered up to the *there*'.[1] Every one of us has certainly at some time or other wished he could change places with someone else who is more gifted and successful. And, on the other hand, when we have seen some unfortunate friend who has missed his vocation or made an unhappy marriage, we have perhaps made the remark that we would not care to change places with him or that we would not like to be in his shoes. Remarks of this kind show that it would be perfectly conceivable for us to exchange our identities. If I stand today in a relation of 'being mine' to this human body and to the whole world of consciousness which goes with it, why should I not stand tomorrow in the same relation to another human body with all the experiences it has amassed? Why should it not be possible to go to sleep tonight as a German citizen and wake up tomorrow as somebody quite different, perhaps as the Dalai-Lama in Tibet or the Mikado in Japan? The notion of metempsychosis or reincarnation, which Lessing and Goethe championed so cordially, appealing to the authority of Pythagoras and Plato and all the sages of the Orient, could not after all have arisen in the first place if it had not been entirely possible to conceive that one might perhaps at one's death give up the relation in which one stands to the body which one calls 'my' body and subsequently assume the same relation to a different body and with it the whole destiny and the whole world of consciousness of another. In the first volume of this work reference was made to the light-hearted experiment carried out by the Baron in the comedy *Jeppe on the Hill* by the Danish dramatist Ludvig Holberg, which is very popular in Denmark and frequently revived. The yokel Jeppe is found lying drunk on the public highway and the Baron has him dressed in fine clothes and put into a magnificent four-poster bed. The climax of the

[1] Martin Heidegger, *Sein und Zeit* (*Being and Time*).

play, which in a good performance always brings the house down, is the moment when the yokel awakes from his slumbers and really believes at first that he has been miraculously transposed into another body and another existence. He asks in his astonishment: 'Where is my wife? Where are my children? Where is my house? And—where is Jeppe?' It would be possible to make this experiment *mutatis mutandis* with each one of us. Every one would think it conceivable that he had undergone a metabasis and been removed to another position in space and located in another body to which he was now attached in the same way as he had hitherto been attached to his first body. The very fact that this experiment can be conducted or at least imagined shows clearly enough that I involuntarily distinguish my actual self from the 'there' into which I have been 'cast'. I know that I myself am something other than the rôle which has been assigned to me by my being attached by my destiny to this human body and by my being obliged to play out this happy or unhappy, exalted or very humble part on the stage of world history until the bitter end.

Reference must also be made in this connexion to a fact which plays a decisive part in the occultist explanation of death; this is the so-called excursion. The viewpoint of the observer is here transferred to a position which lies outside his body. This being beside oneself is sometimes called bilocation. A simple example will make this clear. The well-known doctor, Marcinowski, tells how his bicycle upset and he tumbled off and apparently fell down unconscious. 'Now,' he says, 'I noticed something very odd. My consciousness was localized outside my body and remained fixed in space about two feet away from the place where I was when I was first overcome by fear on seeing that I was certain to fall. I saw myself from the back, quite clearly and distinctly and comparatively calmly; I saw my back and the back of my head and the whole crash and even the rear wheel of the bicycle, all from behind—in short, I saw everything. I knew a severe fracture of the skull was inevitable. At the same time there was present in my consciousness out there the notion that this must not happen and indeed would not happen. I had the

feeling that the fall was now being controlled from this clearly
conscious authority in such a way that the only consequence
was a splitting of the pelvis at the symphysis.'[1]

No direct self-contradiction is at first involved in this change
in the central viewpoint from which one looks at the objective
world. No objection against the possibility of such a change
can be raised by logical thought. But there is a second point
which is of still far greater importance to us in this connexion.
Even from the point of view of natural science, from the point
of view of the objective study of the world, there can be no
objection against the possibility of such a transference. For if
a change of this kind took place, it would not in any way affect
the actual state of the objective world. If I were to exchange
identities with you or with anybody else, that would in no way
disturb the world of scientific research. From the objective
point of view everything would remain as it was. Indeed the
objective study and description of the data and laws of
genetics, characterology, typology or pathology makes a point
of leaving out of account whether it is you or I or some other
known or unknown person who typifies a certain hereditary
condition or presents an interesting clinical example of a
particular disease. Even if I am myself engaged in research
and observe myself and experiment upon myself, I deliberately disregard the fact that I am here myself the object of the
experiment. That is merely an incidental circumstance which
may, according to the case, facilitate or impede the establishment of objective conclusions. My body, too, and my destiny
and my psychological make-up, are for me in this case always
merely specimens illustrating general laws and general relations which I wish to investigate. Thus it makes no difference
to the objective data if the rôles are interchanged. Looking at
it objectively, in surveying the data, the point from which they
are observed is entirely indifferent. And so from the objective
point of view there is no obstacle in the way of exchanging the
position from which I see the world.

From the point of view of objective science, then, it ought
really to be possible for such an exchange to take place at any

[1] Communicated, together with other similar cases, in E. Mattiesen's book,
Das persönliche Überleben des Todes (Personal Survival after Death), Vol. I.

moment without friction or difficulty. Oddly enough that is not the case. This brings us to the fact which most clearly shows that our actual self, with which Fichte is concerned in the *Theory of Science*, belongs to another sphere than the whole world which Heidegger calls the 'available' (*das Vorhandene*) and which displays itself before our eyes in space. Until now we have spoken only of the first general existential proposition, the assertion that each one of us, as soon as he has entered life, is 'delivered up' to a certain 'there' and brought into relation with a concrete component part of the objective world. But now we must add a second existential proposition, which is far more striking even than the first and which is not by any means a necessary and evident corollary to it. I have no possibility of changing or exchanging the 'there' into which I am cast. Such an exchange would indeed in itself be quite easily conceivable and there would be no obstacle to it from the point of view of natural science. But here we come up against an insuperable barrier, an impossibility. This impossibility necessarily goes far deeper than anything which is impossible in logic, for instance the proposition: twice two is five, or anything which is technically impossible because of the governing laws of nature, for example, the suspending of the law of gravity. The impossibility lies in the fact that I am not able to change the position in which I am placed within this world. I did not choose this position myself. Otherwise I might perhaps have been more careful in the selection of my parents and grandparents. I simply found myself in this position; my attachment to this body, this genetic nexus, this nation and homeland, all is imposed upon me either as an unmerited good fortune or as an inescapable burden, as the case may be. My being cast into this position is quite independent of all my own decisions. My lot has been decided here without any intervention on my part.

And so I can still not bring about any alteration in this decision. It is possible that I have no more urgent wish than to be released from this bondage, which has after all come upon me through no fault of mine. I may yearn with every fibre of my heart to escape from this body and this human destiny which is imposed upon me, as a prisoner serving a life sentence yearns to leave his cell. I curse the day when I was born. It is all of no avail. I cannot alter my position or exchange it for another. I am bound to it with iron chains as Prometheus was bound to the rock. I am irrevocably confined within my own sphere of being (*Ichraum*) and consequently just as hopelessly excluded from your sphere of being or from the sphere of being of anyone else to whom I stand in any kind of relation. Thus I can never really enter into the world of another—not even that of my closest friend. How I would like to enter into your mind completely, in order really to do justice to your way of thinking, or simply out of psychological interest, in order for once really to see someone else's mentality from within! But here I am faced with insuperable barriers. The 'ever-strange Thou', as Grisebach calls it, places an insurmountable obstacle in the way of my knowing it. The necessity which confronts us here is not, as we have seen, a purely logical one, like the proposition: twice two is four. There is no logical difficulty about conceiving such a change. I can picture to myself in the most glowing colours what it would be like if I were to go to sleep tonight as an old man and wake up again in the morning as a happy child which I can see playing with other children in front of my windows. Nor is it a physical necessity like, for example, the inheriting of certain genetic characteristics in accordance with the Mendelian law. We are faced here with a third kind of necessity, one which differs fundamentally both from logical and from physical necessity and which is denoted in all the highly developed languages by an archetypal word, $\mu o\hat{\imath}\rho a$, *fatum*, *urd* or fate. But this word is not an answer to the question why I am bound to this position. It is itself no more than an expression of the ultimate question which confronts us now and which nobody can escape.

The necessity which compels me here cannot be objectivised any more than the relation itself with which we are here concerned. It cannot be deduced in accordance with logical or physical laws from the primary forms of the objective world. It cannot be examined with the aid of a microscope or telescope or photography. I can observe psychologically my notions, thoughts, feelings and volitional impulses, and measure their duration and intensity. In particular I can observe the complete dependence of the entire consciousness which I call 'my' consciousness upon certain processes in the body which I call 'my' body. A slight injury to my eyeball, such as a shell-splinter may cause, will perhaps immediately blind me. All the colourful splendour of the visible world around me may in an instant have been swallowed up in night. A head wound, injuring the cerebral cortex, may at one blow destroy a whole section of my store of conscious impressions, for example my linguistic memory. I may explain this dependence of the life of the mind upon the brain in material-istic terms and say that consciousness is only an incidental effect produced by material processes, like the flash of the spark which accompanies the circulation of an electric current. Or again I may adopt the standpoint of psycho-physical paral-lelism and say that cerebral changes and consciousness are two aspects of one and the same process, two forms in which a single event is expressed simultaneously, just as one and the same thought can be expressed in two different languages. Which of these two explanations is correct is a question which in the present context can still be left completely open; our choice makes no difference at all in understanding the peculiar relationship which we are here investigating. Whether I regard the connexion between 'my' body and 'my' world of consciousness as a causal dependence or as a parallelism be-tween two forms of expression of the same thing, the con-nexion which is here variously interpreted is in any case a link between two contents both of which are placed before me equally objectively, and both of which stand in the same relation to me. It is 'my' body of which I am here examining the cerebral process, and it is 'my' world of consciousness which is related to this body. In either case what I observe is never more than the object confronting me. It is not my *self*.

A psychological or physiological description does not con-cern itself at all with the fact which is alone important here, the fact that this body and this consciousness are related to me myself by an invisible line. This bridge, linking a point in the space of visibility with an invisible point, lies beyond the range of psychology and physiology. And yet this obscure point where the line ends, while steadily refusing to submit to any scientific methods of observation, is still not an *x*, fading away in the mist; it is rather for each one of us the most real of the realities with which we have to deal. Our existence comprises the whole destiny of our life; and we can make very definite assertions about this unobservable *ens realissimum*, assertions for which we claim general validity. It is evident that this reality belongs to a region lying outside three-dimensional space.

If one draws attention to this enigma of our personal individual existence and to the pivotal significance which it confers upon the ego, one may be mistakenly supposed to be defending individualism, the rights of the personality in opposition to the communal groups which would like to claim us for their own. It might seem as though we wished to speak in favour of fostering individual peculiarities, but this would be a misunderstanding, for what has been said has nothing to do with anything of this kind. It transcends the antithesis between individualism and socialism. The person whose destiny is my destiny may be a member of a mass of persons in which each individual resembles the others both inwardly and outwardly like so many peas in a pod or like so many grains of sand in the Sahara Desert. He may be Convict No. 1077 amid the tens of thousands of convicts in a prison camp, all of them wearing the same prison garb and all of them marching out to work every morning in perfect step in the great working-party column. Not one of them is irreplaceable. Each of them can readily be replaced by another who will fulfil exactly the same function. If one of them collapses and dies, another one, with the same look on his face, will immediately take his place. But it is precisely when things are like this, when 'the man of the masses is on the march', that the fundamental fact which alone concerns us here becomes all the clearer, the enigmatic fact that I, a number amidst millions of other numbers, am tied to precisely this particular number for the whole long span of a human lifetime and cannot change places with anyone else I care to think of.

Rilke describes in his *Malte* how people die in masses in the great hospitals of a gigantic city. 'Deaths are at present taking place in 559 beds. It is like a factory, of course; and naturally, with this enormous output, the individual death is not a very finished article. But that is not what we are after. What we want is mass production. Who cares nowadays about a well worked-out death? . . . It is becoming more and more unusual for anyone to want a death of his own. My God! That is all there is to it. One comes along, finds one's life ready-made and needs only to put it on. . . . And one dies the way one happens to die; one dies the death appropriate to the illness one has—for now that we know all the diseases we also know that the various forms of death belong to the complaints and not to the patients; the patient has practically no part to play.' The simple matter of fact to which I refer when I utter the word 'I' or the word 'my' does not in any way depend upon whether I succeed in dying the 'great' death, my 'own' death, the 'mature' death, or, like most people today, only the 'little' death, or upon whether my existence has been 'un-actual' because throughout my life I have, as Heidegger and Jaspers put it, been merged in the general impersonal 'one' and have not found my way home to my 'actual existence'. What matters here is rather the simple and for that very reason quite overwhelming fact that, amongst the 559 beds in which deaths are taking place tonight, precisely bed No. 487 is *my* bed and not your bed or anybody else's bed and that for tonight *I* am on the list. This fact simply exists, whether I like it or not. I may feel very unhappy about it; or I may attempt to regard it as being devoid of all significance and try to take up the position which Ernst Jünger adopted in his earlier period at the time of the first world war. We are now after all, according to Jünger's view at that time, in the final phase of the 'total mobilization' of man. Technological per-fection has mobilized the entire world in the shape of the 'worker' and provides the means of finally accomplishing the welding together of the masses into a fighting organism. This is the death sentence for any form of individual existence and necessitates the complete and unreserved sacrifice of the autonomous personality and submission to the superior whole. But whatever valuation I may place upon my separate exist-ence, it is in any case my destiny to be tied to this individuality. I can say like Plato that I am eternally thankful to the gods for two things, firstly that I was born a human being and secondly that I was born in the time of Socrates. But I may also revile my lot in having been born here and now as a stupid coincidence, wishing only that I may be rid as quickly as possible of this burdensome existence and that I may 'drop out' as soon as I can. Yet in either case I am confronted with the unsolved riddle of why it is precisely to this position that I am tied.

All this has brought us to a reality which presents itself to each one of us, including the natural scientist, even before we begin to observe, experiment and calculate. This reality is my personal ego, the *I* of which I am always already aware before any objective knowledge enters my mind. If we wish to define this reality exactly, we must analyse it into two coefficients, a *constant* and a *variable* factor. The *constant* factor is this ego itself, which I can clearly distinguish from the destiny which binds me for the duration of my life to this body and to this position within the world of experience. The fact that I can distinguish my *self* from this destiny of mine does not mean, as Plato thought it meant, that I could also exist independently of my body. Whether such a separate existence is possible or not is another question. Yet the ego, which can be distinguished from the corporeal being, is nevertheless that which Plato called the 'soul' and to which the poet of the twenty-second psalm gave the pregnant title of 'my only one' (Ps. 22.20). This ego, this solitary soul, was not designed or chosen by me. I received it passively; and for that reason it is not within my control. I cannot rid myself of my *self*. Nor can I decide what is to become of me after the death of my body, whether I am to survive or to be extinguished. That does not depend on my wishes; I have no say in the matter. Alongside this constant factor of my ego there is also a *variable* factor which is likewise outside my control. This is the attachment of my constant *self* to a definite position in the world of experience, namely to the position in space and time in which the body is situated which I call *my* body. There is no necessary reason why I should not be tied to another position, another body, without this involving the replacement of my ego by another ego. A 'metempsychosis', a transference of one and the same soul from one body to another, is thus perfectly conceivable, although in consequence of the attachment which our destiny imposes upon us we have no means of bringing it about. But just because it is conceivable we must preserve the distinction between the variable factor of our attachment to our present body from the constant factor of our personal existence.

5. THE ENCOUNTER WITH THE THOU

In the preceding chapters our attention has been directed in the first place to two factors which are antecedent to the entire field of scientific investigation. The first is a *reality* and the second a *relation* in which this reality stands. The *reality,* which cannot be approached by the scientific method, is the non-objectivisable ego. The *relation* is the connexion between the ego and the objective world. For it has become evident that the connecting line, too, which starts from the darkened space where the spectator sits and terminates in the light-filled world of objects at the point to which I am attached by my destiny, lies within the dark region of non-objectivity. The problem of why I am tied to precisely this position within the objective plane and not to any other position 'lies on this side of' the whole range of scientific observation and calculation.

All this still does not exhaust the list of what is antecedent to the field of scientific enquiry; for we have spoken in this connexion of only one of the relations in which the ego is involved, namely the relation between the I and the It, between the subject and the objective world. There still remains the second and equally important relation, the encounter with the Thou. If we survey the course of the history of ideas in the West, we are immediately struck by the fact that, although the I, with its sovereign independence from the objective world opposing it, was discovered very early, it was nevertheless only very late, indeed only during the last few decades, that philosophers really became conscious of the encounter with the Thou and of the whole multitude of problems with

which this encounter confronts us. Why that is so becomes
clear to us only if we cast a brief glance at the course of the
history of philosophy.

The great discoverer in the West of the ego and of its
separateness from the whole objective world was Plato.
According to Plato the whole world of visible phenomena is
involved in continual change. Face to face with this whole
transitory world there stands the 'soul', the Archimedean
external fulcrum, the one invisible reality. The visible
changes, but the invisible remains. The soul is indivisible
and is therefore, Plato concluded, an indestructible substance.
In contrast to the world of phenomena, the soul participates in
true, unchanging being. This Greek conception was taken up
again in a new form by the German idealists. Kant's *Critique
of Pure Reason* begins by defining it critically in such a way as
to exclude all the metaphysical consequences which the Greeks
had drawn from it. But, even in this critical formulation,
idealism at the very outset of the battle took up a position
which rendered it unassailable from the direction of any of
the experimental sciences, including the rapidly advancing
physical sciences. The starting-point of Kant's *Critique of
Pure Reason* is 'the ego of transcendental apperception'
which achieves the 'synthesis' in which are rooted all the
categories of understanding that alone render experience
possible. But now there arises the point in Kant's system
which from the outset excludes any consideration of the problem of the encounter with the Thou. The ego which observes
the data that 'affect' our senses is not, according to Kant, an
individual person such as might coexist with other persons so
that there would then be several egos. For in that case these
egos would necessarily be numerable; but only those things are
numerable which confront us as objects. Thus the ego of
transcendental apperception can be present only in the singular. It is in 'consciousness in general' that we as individual
persons participate when we think and when by means of the
categories of understanding we penetrate into the world of
experience. The ego is like a central sun, shining in solitude
high above the world and illuminating the world for us with
its radiance if we share in its light. Rickert, who has worked

D

out these fundamental Kantian conceptions more thoroughly than anyone else in his book *The Object of Knowledge,* calls this single ego the 'epistemological subject' in contradistinction to the physical subject, the psychophysical subject and the psychical subjects which belong to the objective world.

In this way there is secured a 'point outside', which is placed from the outset beyond the range of scientific explanation because it precedes it and alone 'makes it possible in the first place'. It is the solitary point which is antecedent to all experience and which strictly speaking should not even be called real; for according to Kant reality means 'being comprehended in the context of experience'. There is no need for us to attain this point by means of scientific enquiry; for indeed as thinking beings we already occupy this position outside the world 'before all experience', i.e. before experimental science sets to work. Consequently no sort of natural science can call it in question again. At the first stage of critical idealism this 'point outside' is simply a point about which no further assertion can be made; but then there comes the transition from critical to speculative idealism brought about by Fichte, and here the unassailable position which Kant had taken up, prior to all experience, is very considerably strengthened. For now the thinking subject becomes a free volitional ego dwelling in solitary state high above the emergence and evanescence of worlds. Since as a 'relative ego' I, too, in my deepest essence am one with the 'absolute ego', the subject to which the whole world is object, I can confront undaunted every vicissitude which befalls my physical body. I myself am completely untouched by all that. I am cut off from it by a deep gulf. I can face 'the measureless cosmos at the very thought of which my sense-bound soul trembles' and cry: 'It is you who change, not I; all your metamorphoses are no more than a stage-play; I shall for ever soar unscathed above the wreckage of your puppets.' The fate which befalls my body cannot disturb me deeply. I can face the universe and say: 'This body is yours and is transitory like everything that is yours; but I am not this body. I myself shall soar freely above its wreckage, and its dissolution will be my stage-play.' Even the destruction of the whole cosmos is merely a spectacle at which the ego looks on. 'When the newest-born of the millions of suns which shine above my head has long since poured out its last spark of light, I shall still be, unscathed and untransformed, the same person that I am today.' And even if fresh suns have come into being and the latest of them has long since poured out its last spark of light, yet I shall still be, unscathed and untransformed, the same who I am today, and my will, too, will be what it is today—my duty.' This autocratic attitude, in which the relative ego as an incarnation of the absolute participates in the supra-mundane character of God, is possible obviously solely because philosophy had taken cognizance of only the first of the two fundamental facts, namely that the thinking subject cannot be objectivised, while no real attention had yet been paid to the second fundamental fact, which forms a salutary counterpoise to man's delusion that he is like God, namely the fact that this ego which cannot be observed as an object is nevertheless chained to a definite position in the transitory world of phenomena.

It is only during our own time, in about 1930, with the latest change in philosophy from neo-Kantianism to the so-called existential philosophy and fundamental ontology—the names are relatively unimportant here—that the second fact has received the serious attention of philosophers and has brought about a radical change in the whole conception of reality, a change which in one all-important respect has carried us far beyond idealism. Behind this new trend in the development of philosophy, which received its first impetus from Kierke-gaard and has been brought into prominence by such thinkers as Heidegger and Jaspers, there lies an oppressive awareness of the unalterable destiny which weighs mercilessly upon the shoulders of modern man and the like of which the idealists never knew. It is true that Heidegger, just like the idealists, contrasts our 'being there', the existence of our self, with anything that is merely 'available' (*vorhanden*) or 'at hand' (*zuhanden*). Existence is an entirely different 'mode of being' from that of the whole objective world. And yet this existence does not soar freely in solitary state high above all experience. Existence ('being there') is rather in itself always a 'being in the world', a 'being cast into one's *there*'. That is why it possesses the 'character of a burden'. It is 'anxiety', 'uneasiness', 'being worried to death'. Yet as soon as the enigmatic bond has become visible, which ties us to a definite position in the world so that we have to follow the movements of this position just as the passengers follow the movements of a ship, my isolation from the objective world ceases, but that is not all. A second isolation is called in question, that which for the idealists was implied in the principle that the 'epistemological subject' can exist only in the singular because, after all, only objective things have number. This inference, that because the ego is not objective it can exist only in the singular, is logically absolutely cogent and evident. But it is precisely at this point that logic is incomprehensibly refuted by the reality of our existence. For just as certainly as I know that in contrast to anything merely 'available' (*vorhanden*) I possess existence (*Dasein*), I know also that 'existence' is not merely 'being in the world'. 'Existence (*Dasein*) is also essentially coexistence (*Mitsein*)', or, as Jaspers says, 'I exist only in communication with another'. 'Even the isolation (*Alleinsein*) of the existence,' says Heidegger, 'is coexistence in the world. The absence of another is possible only in and for a coexistence. Isolation is a deficient mode of coexistence. The possibility of isolation is the proof of coexistence.'

But is it not an essential characteristic of the transcendental ego that it exists only in the singular, since it is agreed that only objects have number? This fundamental idealistic principle must surely not be abandoned. But it is precisely if we keep it firmly in mind that we clearly see the whole paradox of the actual situation which we intend to convey when we use the word 'thou'. 'An audible discord disturbs the harmonious chorus of isolated human beings,' says Grisebach in his book *Actuality* (*Gegenwart*). Something dark and strange breaks in upon the quiet, ordered world of the ego and shakes its foundations. In what does this something strange consist, which forces its way in, troubles me and calls in question the fundamental logical presuppositions upon which my isolated thinking rests? We become fully conscious of this only if we do not forget the second fundamental fact from which we set out upon this whole discussion, the fact that my ego is tied to a definite position in the world of experience. The picture of the whole world which I necessarily form for myself from this particular central vantage-point is all at once disturbed and called in question by the coming on the scene of a second ego which is as irremovably and unexchangeably welded to another position as I am to mine. From this there arises a world which has two centres and yet which logically can have only one centre. For each of us, both you and I, must make the same demand and the same claim, namely, that we are *the* centre, the only standpoint from which everything is seen correctly. The non-objective seeing point is located in two positions, yet it *can* only be located in one position and *can* only be one seeing point. Two 'egos' is an impossible expression even from the linguistic point of view. The word 'ego' can only be used in the singular; for otherwise it loses its non-objective character and becomes an object possessing number like other objects. And yet we are forced to use the word 'ego' in the plural! We are so accustomed to this paradoxical situation that in everyday life we are already scarcely aware of the contradiction which it involves. We notice it all the more clearly for this in all the crises of human intercourse.

Whenever two people talk together or go about together over a fairly long period, there arises an atmosphere of electric tension which is from time to time always discharged in some violent thunderstorm that disturbs the peaceful course of their relations with one another. The continual misunderstanding, failing to make oneself clear and missing the point, and all the perpetual tensions and frictions which every day result from this, do not arise as is always supposed from the obstinacy, pushfulness and self-assertiveness of certain intolerable individuals. The ultimate root from which all these repeated conflicts between individuals, families and nations grow is the structure of the 'coexistence' into which we are all thrown, because each must necessarily be the centre of the whole, the only vantage-point from which the world can really be seen. Because each alike must claim to be this centre, coexistence is not a peaceful juxtaposition; it is not a case of 'both and', but an abrupt 'either or'. We shall have to return again to this disharmony in our human existence when we come to our final section and are faced with the question whether the discord running through the entire world can be resolved. Our present immediate purpose is merely to establish a position 'on this side of' the whole range of scientific research so that we may have a basis for our discussion with contemporary natural science. The fact that the Thou, the 'ever-strange other person', together with our tense and heavily charged relation to him, has now entered into the field of vision of philosophical study has meant that the unassailable position which is immune from the intervention of natural science has been considerably broadened and reinforced in comparison with that which was maintained by Kant and Fichte and their successors. The basis upon which we can take our stand has become firmer.

The new situation may be represented graphically by developing an analogy of which we have already made use. Previously, in the period of idealism, only one person sat in the darkened auditorium and watched the cosmic drama unfolding on the brightly lighted stage of objective reality. Now the darkened auditorium has filled and contains many persons; they cannot indeed see each other but each of them is nevertheless aware of the presence of his neighbour. They push each other this way and that. Each one lays claim to the one favoured position in the middle of the stalls exactly opposite the centre of the stage. In the idealist conception of reality encounters between persons belonged to the world of objects and so to the field of scientific investigation, just like encounters between billiard balls knocking together on a billiard table or encounters between astronomical bodies attracting and repelling one another in the cosmic space. For this reason idealism had not yet remarked the paradoxical state of affairs which confronts us in every encounter with the Thou. It was not yet conscious at all of the problem implied in the fact that every encounter between the I and the Thou is a meeting of two subjects each of which is as completely isolated as the other. Jaspers defines community as 'the meeting of one solitary individual soul with another solitary individual soul'. Idealism was still quite unaware of the inconceivable character of this encounter between two lonely souls; it is inconceivable because the two subjects, as we have seen, are mutually exclusive, since each of them must necessarily claim to be the centre of the world. And yet, although each one tries to exclude and invalidate the other, they have need of each other and cannot exist without each other. This fundamental fact of our existence does not indeed become completely clear until the word 'I' is employed not in the vague and general sense of personality and individuality but with the exact meaning which we took as our starting-point in the first chapter of these introductory remarks. The proposition: 'I am' signifies that by virtue of a destiny to which my attitude is purely passive I must for all time be precisely this person and no other person, that is to say not you or anyone else that I might in the nature of things just as well be. I am therefore I only by dint of drawing a line between myself and you, contrasting myself with you, and differentiating and distinguishing myself from you and everybody else. The affirmative proposition 'I am Subject A' is thus always simply the converse of the negative proposition 'I am not Subject B or any one of the innumerable other subjects which also exist'. The contrast with the Thou and with all other subjects is therefore essential to the ego. In this sense it is possible to say that one cannot exist in isolation at all. 'I exist only by virtue of you'; I discover myself only 'against you', that is to say in the thousand and one intensely charged relations in which I stand to you. My ego is like a creeper to which it is essential that it should entwine and grow up some object lying outside itself. If it does not find it, it must lie and wither on the ground. Thus the ego cannot exist in isolation; the 'audible dissonance' which I find in the presence of the Thou is therefore at the same time the only element in which I can exist; it is the indispensable condition of my being.

We will not pursue here the consequences which result from this state of tension for our entire judgment of the world in which we are living. We are still concerned in this connexion only with the 'impregnable stronghold' which is prior to the objective world of experience and must form the basis for our settlement of accounts with natural science. Although at this point it was necessary only to touch upon it briefly, there is revealed to us here an entire world of invisible relations still 'on this side of' the whole range of physical and biological observations and assertions. For indeed the two of us, you and I, can communicate with each other only by means of our two bodies to which we are puzzlingly attached for the whole duration of our lives; and these bodies, with their sensory and motor nerves, their senses and speech organs, may be subjected, down to the minutest constituent parts, to medical examination. They can be placed under the microscope, recorded and analysed. And not only our bodies. Even our mental experiences, our trains of associations and our dreams, can be analysed psychologically. For example, one can follow the method of Jung in investigating their origins in the individual and collective subconscious. Yet we ourselves, you and I, who play upon these wonderful instruments, our animate bodies, and communicate with one another by means of them, we still cannot be objectivised at all. The anatomist and even the psychologist see nothing of our essential selves. The meeting which takes place between my solitary soul and your solitary soul may indeed be expressed physically and be reflected in psychological experiences which can be scientifically objectivised; but the encounter itself is prior to all that. It cannot be filmed or held fast on a photographic plate. It is true that the inner struggles, the mental strife, the repressed complexes and the abreactions, in which this archetypal conflict finds its expression in the mind, do indeed appear objectively and can therefore be psychologically analysed. But the purpose of all these analyses in psychotherapy and depth-psychology demands that they should always treat the persons on whom the experiments are conducted as objectively given 'human guinea-pigs' or 'clinical cases', from whose behaviour it is possible to deduce general laws and rules for a therapeutic process. The special circumstance, which is the only one relevant to our present discussion, that this clinical case is not just any old case but *my* fate or *your* fate or somebody else's fate is not taken into account at all in this analysis. It may happen that I as a doctor am my own patient or that I experiment on myself in the diagnosis of dreams. In many cases this may make the diagnosis easier, but in other cases it may upset and impede it because I am 'prejudiced' and no longer approach the object of the experiment altogether objectively. One sees this already when the doctor has to treat as a patient the person who is personally closest to him, his own wife.

But whether this incidental circumstance that the clinical case is my own case facilitates or impedes the objective investigation, the fact remains that it does not in any case affect the objective analysis as such. Objective investigation according to the methods of natural science is not in any way concerned with the fact that I am attached by an incomprehensible destiny to this particular case. The psychological researcher does not bother his head with the grave and difficult question which is raised by this mysterious fact: Why is it that I have no possibility of being freed from my attachment to this one human destiny? Why is it that I am fettered to this one position within the world of experience, just like a criminal who is condemned to lifelong imprisonment and will never again leave his cell? Why can I not change places with you or anybody else who has drawn a luckier number? And that is why the psychologist cannot concern himself either with all the electric tension which arises from this unresolved problem whenever we meet. It is precisely this factor, this unsolved problem and this inner tension, which is all-important in the region which we have now entered, the region of encounters between the I and the Thou.

6. THE WILL AND EVENTS IN THE WORLD

In the two preceding chapters a region has been revealed to us in which we are all situated but which lies beyond the range of the method of investigation proper to natural science. The great significance which this non-objectivisable region possesses, not only for our knowledge but for our entire life, becomes clear to us only if we now extend the scope of our considerations to include the most important aspect of reality, namely the fact that the world of experience in which we are located is not at rest in a static condition but advancing in time and involved in continuous change. In the uninterrupted flood of time, which carries us away together with the whole world, there lies hidden the deepest mystery of our existence. We can understand this underlying form of our existence only when we have understood the peculiar relation between the two spaces in which we simultaneously live. Let us for the moment leave ourselves out of consideration and direct our attention to time as it appears to us in objective experience! The objective passage of time, into which natural science classes events, is 'physical time', i.e. a measurable length, extending in a definite direction. The points lying on this directional line are arranged in a definite sequence within the length of time. This is the series t, t_1, t_2, t_3 . . . t_n, in which the points from t to t_n follow one another in a fixed chronological order, just as the points on a spatial line follow one another in a constant spatial order. It differs from the spatial line only in that it is a 'one-way street' which can be traversed only in one direction. The points on the directional time-line are all of equal significance. The length of the span of time is measured just as the length of the spatial line is measured, i.e. by taking as one's basis an arbitrarily chosen unit, for example, the second. That is the picture which time presents if I consider it apart from myself. A completely different picture of reality arises, however, if I no longer leave myself out of account but relate my own existence to this conception of time. As we have seen, I myself am irremovably and unexchangeably related by a necessity of my destiny to a definite position in the world of experience. From the non-objective space in which I stand there runs, so to speak, a line which extends to this one definite position in the world of objects. In this way this position acquires a special significance deriving from a different dimension. Since the world of experience is not in a state of rest but continually moving forwards in the flow of time, one point on the time line, although objectively in alignment with all the other points on the line, in this way suddenly acquires a special significance which distinguishes it from the rest of the series. It acquires the character of being *now*. I can express what is meant by *now* only by starting from myself and applying a demonstrative pronoun to the point of time at which I am living, together with all those who are my contemporaries. That is 'our' time. 'We' are destined to be living today. It may be that we have already at some time wished that *now* could be put back a century, perhaps to the days of Goethe, or put on a century, into a future when those things for which we must now struggle will have been achieved.

Here there is especially clearly revealed the fateful character of the 'placing' (*Setzung*) which determines my existence. Logically nothing would stand in my way if I wished to alter the position where *now* is situated, in order to exchange it for an earlier or later position within the time series; for logically all points in the time series have precisely the same right to be *now*. Even from the standpoint of natural science nothing would prevent the point *now* from being moved forwards or backwards. The laws and relations of nature remain the same whether the researcher's 'present' is the time at which Galileo made his experiments with the pendulum on the leaning tower of Pisa or the time at which Max Planck established the quantum theory. That the conditions of existence of the ego do not derive from the objective world of experience but from a different dimension is shown by the very fact that a kind of necessity comes into play here which is neither logical necessity nor physical necessity. Even though there are neither logical nor scientific objections to the removal of the point *now* to any other position one may prefer, yet I am irremovably and unexchangeably bound with fetters of iron to this position which is 'my' present. It is not of the least use to me if in a mood of romantic nostalgia I dream my way back into times long past or if with bold imagination I skip the intervening years which separate me from a better future. I am irremovably attached to this 'my' present. In this way the point *now* is raised above the whole series of points in the time sequence and made the *time centre*; and thus the whole picture of time is altered, for henceforward we must regard the entire stream of events in time from the standpoint of *now*. We see from this that everything which is past must once have been present; everything which has become history has at some time passed through the point *now*. Consequently, if we consider the whole sequence of events from the standpoint of *now*, we can compare time with a long rope which is wound round a drum and which is reeled off as the drum turns. The drum is always in the same place. It is held fast in this place by an invisible hand. As the rope is gradually wound off, each part of it moves farther and farther from the place where the drum is. In exactly the same way, every event, after being present, becomes an occurrence which has just taken place and is therefore still fresh in our memory. Today becomes yesterday. Then the event continues to recede and fades away more and more in the grey mist of the past. Nothing can become history which has not previously been the present. Thus, if we stand at the point *now*, we are at the source from which everything has proceeded which was and from which everything will proceed which is still to come. The *now* is the fruitful womb which brings forth all that takes place in the world. That is why everything which has been accomplished is still contained latently in the point *now*; for otherwise it could not have proceeded from it. The *now* is filled with history, which still vibrates within it. And everything which is to come is contained within it as an inexhaustible wealth of possibilities, like the rope which is still rolled round the drum and still has to be wound off. Or, to change the simile, the 'eternal now', the *nunc aeternum*, is like a deep spring from which a river runs continually. The whole past is mysteriously contained in this spring; for otherwise it could not have streamed forth from it. But in the depths of the spring there also lies the whole future, as a possibility which is still unrealized. It lies there like an undiscovered treasure. It sleeps there like Emperor Barbarossa in the dark depths of the Kyffhäuser.

This has brought us to a conception of the essential nature of time which is quite the opposite of the objective conception of time from which we set out. In the objective conception the *now* was merely a fortuitous, unmarked point in the endless series of essentially exactly similar points, the sum total of which constitutes the time line; but in this other conception the one single point *now* has incorporated into itself the whole of time, past and future, because potentially it carries within itself all that has been and all that is to be. The

whole content of time is comprised in each of these two conceptions, both in the objective time series, in which all the
points of time are equally privileged, and in the non-objective
time, in which the sequence of temporal events wells forth
from the eternal *now* as though from a primordial fountainhead. But this content is differently arranged within the two
kinds of time according to their contrasting structures. In
the objective time series the point *now* is an arbitrary point,
one of an infinite number of successive points of time, like a
bead in a necklace. The time line is like a one-way street,
leading from the most distant past into the most distant future.
The point *now* moves forward along this endless road like a
lonely traveller. Where he happens to be at any particular
moment is a matter of no importance or consequence. Strictly
speaking, from the point of view of the objective conception of
time, it makes no essential difference in which of the two
possible directions time is traversed. To make this clear one
need only run through a reel of film backwards instead of forwards for a change, so that the single instantaneous photographs of which it is composed appear in the reverse order.
The resulting picture is amusing. People go hurrying backwards just as excitedly as they had previously hurried forwards.
The horses do not pull the cart, but push it along backwards.
The ravens fly through the air tail foremost, and so forth and
so forth. When we see a film in reverse like this (as one was
once projected for us for scientific purposes in Krupp's little
cinema at Essen), it immediately becomes clear to us that, from
the objective point of view, the direction in which the
sequence of temporal events runs could perfectly well be
changed round so that they would follow one another in the
opposite order. At first sight, if we leave ourselves out of
consideration and look only at the objective world, there is no
criterion at all for deciding which of the two directions leads
forwards into the future and which leads backwards into the
past. In order to settle this question within the objective
world, we must first of all look for a signpost with one arm
marked 'To the Future' and the other 'To the Past'. According to Eddington[1] there is, if I leave myself out of account,

[1] A. S. Eddington, *The Nature of the Physical World*, Cambridge 1928.

only one signpost to indicate the direction of time. This signpost is based on a definite measurable physical magnitude, on entropy. According to the second law of thermodynamics, within an isolated system the accumulation of heat is progressively dissipated. Thus the whole tends increasingly towards what is called thermodynamic equilibrium. 'Consequently, of two points in time, t_1 and t_2, the later point is the one at which this process has progressed farther, i.e. the point corresponding to the greater entropy.'

But if we adopt the other, non-objective conception of time, its completely different structure invests with a totally different standing and a totally different significance this same point which, in the objective time series, was only one amongst an infinite number of other points, $t, t_1, t_2, t_3 \ldots$ and so on, and the time direction leading forwards into the future also acquires a meaning wholly different from that of the time direction leading backwards into the past. Here the point *now* is the place touched by eternity, the position in which I am located by an ineluctable necessity. It is the great turning-point, the watershed of time, dividing the course of time into two parts which have quite opposite meanings for our existence. The part which has already passed through the point *now* is, as it were, signed, sealed and delivered; the die is cast. It is in the fossilized state of 'having become' and it cannot be undone. It has become history. 'The past lies in eternal silence.' But whatever has not yet passed through the point *now* is still in the molten phase of becoming. It is still undecided. It is still being fought for. It still contains boundless possibilities. There, as Schiller put it, 'there rest still in the womb of time the happy and unhappy lots yet to be drawn'. These are the two opposing conceptions of time, in which the same universal content is quite differently arranged. These two time pictures are two spaces in which we live simultaneously.

Now it is only when we have a clear picture of this second aspect, which the passage of time in world events presents when it is experienced from the space of non-objectivity, that we fully understand the meaning of another archetypal word in our human language, a word which is of decisive impor-

tance in our whole dispute with natural science. This is the
word 'will' which we use when we say, for example, 'I *will*
not go under. I *will* become a new man. I *will* turn over a
new leaf.' We make a thoroughly clear distinction between
what we call will in sentences of this kind and the words and
deeds which are born of this will. The will, as has already
been said, is the lightning flash, and the deed is the long-
drawn roll of thunder which follows it. Whatever has become
deed belongs to the objective world. It can be observed
objectively and its energy content measured, just as, for
example, the operation of an electric current can. With the
will it is different. The will is prior to all the objective
effects which proceed from it. The existence of the will is not
at all dependent on whether the will is converted into action
or whether its realization is prevented by insuperable
obstacles. Kant's *Fundamental Principles of the Metaphysics of
Ethics* opens with the celebrated sentences: 'It is not possible
to think of anything anywhere in the world, or even anywhere
outside it, which could unrestrictedly be regarded as good,
excepting only a good *will*. . . . The good will is good, not by
virtue of what it performs or accomplishes, nor yet by virtue
of its effectiveness for the achieving of any proposed aim,
but solely by virtue of its willing; in other words, it is good
in itself. Even though, through some special unkindness of
fate or through the meagreness of the gifts bestowed by an
ungenerous nature, this will were quite lacking in the power
to realize its intention, . . . and though only the good *will*
. . . remained, yet it would on its own account still shine like
a jewel, as something which contains its entire value within
itself.' In these sentences Kant quite clearly distinguishes the
'will in itself' from its realization, its consequences on the
objective plane. But if my will is different from anything
that can be observed as its effect in the world of objects, then
it cannot itself be observed objectively at all by other people.
Every volitional decision is an act of self-isolation. Let us
consider, for example, a man in whom there has been matur-
ing the decision to put an end to his life and to cast off the
burden which he can no longer bear. Weighed down with this
grave resolve, he is quite alone as he walks through the laugh-

ing and chattering crowds amid the noisy traffic of a busy city
street.   He is quite alone as he makes his way to a deserted
spot on the bank of a canal where he plans to put his decision
into effect.   But to be thus alone in the knowledge of my
will is not to have objective experience of it.   I do not know
about my will as I know about my body and my whole world
of conceptions and memories.   I cannot look into my will as
I can look, for instance, into the mechanism of a watch if I
open the lid.   My will cannot be objectivised even for me.
And yet I do know about it, and indeed I know about it more
certainly and directly than I know about all the effects which
it produces.

   All this indicates that it is with my will just as it is with my
ego.   My ego, too, I cannot confront objectively, and yet it is
still what is nearest and most intimately known to me.   If this
is also the case with my will, there can be only one explanation.   My will is a particular form of existence of my ego.   In
what does this particular form of existence consist?   This becomes clear to us if we think of the two contrasting forms in
which, as we have seen, the passage of time manifests itself.
The time series in which the events of the world take place,
if we look at it purely objectively and leave the ego out of
consideration, is nothing more than a succession of cosmic
instants which are placed on the time line in a definite
sequence.   It is like a strip of film on which the instantaneous
photographs of what happens are arranged one after the other
in chronological order.   The series of pictures may be looked
at forwards or backwards, but the objective sequence always
remains the same.   No one picture is more important than
another.   But this is true only so long as the film strip is kept
at rest.   The case is altered when the film is passed through the
projector and the drama it represents unfolds before the eyes
of the spectator, who sees it for the first time and follows the
development of the plot with the most intense excitement
and suspense.   Now the ego is present, confronting the drama.
This ego is at every moment linked by a necessity of destiny
with a definite point within the time series.   That is how this
point acquires the special significance of being *now*.   One
instantaneous photograph after another passes through the

point *now*. The *now* is the point on the frontier at which the whole sequence of world events crosses over from the molten state in which it is still undecided to the solid state of the unalterable past in which it sets firm.

The world is passing over with us at every moment into this state of solidification, in which events are signed, sealed and delivered and cannot in any way be altered. We experience this crisis very intensely at times when fateful decisions are being taken in which everything is at stake. Consider, for example, the moments immediately preceding a surgical operation on which our life or death may depend, or the hours just before the outbreak of war, or the anxious minutes waiting for a big air-raid in which it will be decided whether or not a great city, with its hundreds of thousands of human lives, is to be transformed into a mass of rubble. At all such moments we are almost physically aware of the hardly bearable tension at the dividing line between the undecided and the decided condition of the world. Before the line is reached, all possibilities are still open. Everything may still be averted. The millions of men and their wives, mothers and sweethearts, who will be thrown into the depths of misery if war breaks out —they may be saved. At such moments as this, it is as though a monstrous and menacing storm-cloud is lying over the whole face of the earth, but still no lightning flash has struck. On the wireless the latest news is being read and the whole world listens in breathless expectation. Diplomats exchange telegrams. One alarming report follows close on the heels of another. The air is alive with rumours. But the tide may still turn. At the very next moment, however, the door has slammed to. The order for mobilization has been issued. The irresistible avalanche is on the move.

In such hours, when world history is being made, we are merely more intensely conscious than usual of something which is in fact happening over and over again at every moment in the course of world events. We are crossing the frontier together with the whole cosmos, not merely together with all the living creatures which inhabit the earth but also together with all the inorganic elemental particles of which the solar systems are composed. Together with all these we

E

are advancing on an immensely broad front across the border which separates what can still be undone from what has already become part of that history of which it may be said with truth that 'the past lies in eternal stillness'.

Now it is only when we consider the quite inconceivable implications of the decision which is being taken once again at this present cosmic moment, and when we envisage the long frontier line which we are now crossing in common with the entire universe, that we can answer the question which has led us to this whole approach: What is the position of the will in this cosmos which is in a continual state of transformation? The will is indeed, as we have seen, a form of existence of the ego, and the ego is on this side of the objective world of experience. The will thus belongs to the non-objectivisable space to which the ego belongs, the space in which the encounter takes place between the I and the Thou. This encounter, as we saw in the last chapter, creates an atmosphere charged with tensions. The I and the Thou are mutually exclusive, because each of them claims to be the centre of the world; and yet neither can exist without the other. I discover myself only in my meeting with you, and *vice versa*. Now, if the world is not at rest but is moving forward in continuous change in time, it follows that the two positions in the world of experience, the position to which I am related by my destiny and the position to which you are related by yours, must make simultaneously the great movement in which, together and in step with the whole cosmos, we cross the dividing line of which we have already clearly seen the significance. But each of us, both you and I, is linked with a different position within this long boundary line at which the decision about the future is taken. If we disregard the I and the Thou and consider only what can be viewed objectively from outside, then all we shall see will be the objective exterior picture of the sequence of world events. We shall see the unfolding of a process in which one phase of the development makes its appearance after the other.

It is a different matter if we relate to the overall picture the I and the Thou and our encounter at the point *now*. Then we ourselves share in the experience of what is going on, with all its tensions and excitements. Then, all at once, the hidden substratum of world events is revealed. We are shown the inner picture which lies behind the objective outward picture of the process. The tension between the perspectives of two points of vision, each of which necessarily claims to be the centre of the world, can now no longer be merely the conflict between the two views of the world which result when the world is photographed from two opposite vantage-points. These two views cannot indeed ever arise until a decision about a world event has been reached; for only an accomplished event is precipitated in objective form so that it can be looked at from the standpoint of the neutral observer. But at the point *now* the decision about the new conformation of the world has just not yet been taken. The event which we are directly experiencing together has still not assumed an objective form. The struggle to determine this form is still in progress. Consequently, in this molten condition of *now,* the conflict between the I and the Thou takes on quite a new shape. The two of us, you and I, are drawn into the process of becoming, from which a new conformation of the world is to be born. Because of the differing conceptions of the previous conformation of the world which each of us has formed from his own standpoint, we also take up opposite points of view with regard to the conformation of the world which lies in the future. From this there arises a heated conflict between the I and the Thou to influence the fateful decision which at this very moment is to be taken about the future of the world. The *now* is the red-hot forge where the future is to be hammered into shape. *Now* everything is still in a state of flux. Each of us from his own point of view must say: 'I will strike the iron while it is hot.' This struggle between the I and the Thou for the new conformation of the world is precisely what we call will. Just as the I discovers itself only in its opposition to the Thou, so my will becomes will only in opposition to your will. Will exists only in close combat with a counter-will, a combat which sometimes leads to passionate clashes and sometimes dies down for a time in a peace settlement or culminates in the kind of fraternal alliance which is born in the heat of battle.

But it will be objected against this conception that the will does not in fact always arise from conflict with a counter-will. It is in most cases rather a struggle with inanimate matter, with lifeless material, for example the struggle in which a creative artist wrests the statue from a stubborn block of marble which obstinately resists his efforts, or the struggle in which a mountaineer 'masters' the sheer wall of the Eiger, employing every ounce of his will-power, or the fearful struggle in which Sven Hedin, during the most terrible night of his life, making a last desperate effort of will, fought for survival against the sand-storm in the desert of Eastern Turkestan, or the struggle of the bold seafarer against the wind and the waves. Precisely this objection leads us to the fact which it is here most essential to understand. We can perceive the position which the will occupies in the over-all picture of reality only if we regard the world not statically as a motionless state of being but dynamically as a process, in the sense in which a modern atomic physicist has asserted that 'matter is not something being, it is something happening'. It follows from this, if we wish to express ourselves with strict accuracy, that we can say of the block of marble, the Eiger, the desert sand or the ocean wave only that they have just *been* in the particular form in which they confront us. For only what has *been* is precipitated as an object. It is not yet really certain what these material realities will be in another moment, the moment which is being born of the present moment. In very many cases I can forecast it with an extremely high degree of probability; indeed I can calculate it in advance like an eclipse of the sun. But even the extremely high degree of probability which is proper to a good prognosis is never certainty; it is still always separated from absolute certainty by a gulf which has yet to be crossed. An event is never a certainty until it is accomplished, signed, sealed and delivered. Until that has happened, something may occur even at the very last moment to prevent it. There may emerge quite unexpectedly from the unknown depths of the cosmos some factor with which we have not reckoned and which makes hay of our entire forecast. The fact that this possibility is present in all events which occur in time has in all ages led those who hold the reins of power, and who have been gambling with their opponents with the world as the prize, into the temptation to stake everything on one number and at the last moment, when all has seemed to be lost already, to play a final trump, risking everything with a blind and foolhardy trust in the 'last chance' which lies in the fact that the imminent catastrophe has still not actually occurred and that, so long as today is still today, the much desired turn in their luck may yet supervene. The rulers of world history have quite often acted in this way just as a gambler at Monte Carlo acts when he has played away his whole fortune except for a small sum and still tries his luck once more by staking this small sum before finally taking his own life.

From all this we can see that even the most solid things there are in the world, even great boulders or blocks of concrete or hewn stone, are strictly speaking not absolutely invariable quantities but always merely occurrences; even though they have stood, like the pyramids the Pharaohs built, for thousands of years completely unaltered, still at this present moment it is ever anew being decided whether they are to outlast the moment which is to follow or whether their time is up. Because this is so, it is not only with my fellow human beings nor even with living beings in general that I must engage in the invisible close combat in which I wrestle with them for a new conformation of the world. The same mysterious contest may also take place between me and some inorganic substance upon which my fate depends. This apparently lifeless and invariable mass too at every moment passes together with me once again through the stage at which the conformation is decided which it is to possess the moment after. The inorganic world, too, always assumes an objective form only when its conformation is decided. Thus, if I enter into a relation with this substance at the stage of undecidedness, it is still in a non-objective state. It is thus together with me in the same space in which the encounter takes place between the I and the Thou. If, in the course of this invisible contest in which I engage with this substance, the substance happens to endanger my life, that is merely another manifestation of the same conflict which, in the field of human affairs, exists between me and you, between my will and yours, when we wrestle with one another for the future of the world. We can thus understand the remarkable fact that we involuntarily personify or treat as a living being any reality which offers resistance to our will, such as an avalanche or a mass of rubble that tries to overwhelm us. We do not experience it as a life-less mass but as something which is, however distantly, analogous to a human will, as a demonic power against which we hurl ourselves with all our willpower as though we had to deal with a human adversary. That is the case even when we have to abandon the fight against the superior strength of the elements and natural forces, like Sven Hedin in that most terrible night of his expedition when he wrote in his diary: 'Sandhills on all sides. Not a sign of life. My men and the camels are all extremely weak. God help us! ' Even at moments like this we are not simply oppressed by a mechanical force which is stronger than our human will. Even a fatal-istic submission is still a relation between wills, a conflict between a will and a more powerful counter-will, a conflict of which the outcome, as can be seen from the entry in Sven Hedin's diary, is still not finally decided.

All this has been leading us to the conclusion that what we call the will, in contradistinction to impulse and instinct, desire and the experience of pleasure and displeasure, is not an energy within the narrow field of our human organism, existing side by side with the other, far more powerful energies in the world, such as gravity, electricity, magnetism and the chemical and biological forces. If it were that, then the will of us puny human beings would be of no consequence at all for the course of world events. But the invisible force which we designate with the word 'will' is not comprised within the narrow confines of our tiny human existence. For since the volitional ego is non-objectivisable it transcends the whole objective world space and all its spatial dimensions; so the will cannot be localized in the human body, this limited, objective structure—neither in the brain nor in the heart. Admittedly my volitional ego is related by my destiny to this human body. My body is my most important instrument. But the will itself, the volitional I and the volitional Thou, is prior to the whole objective march of world events to which it is related, and consequently lies beyond the range of scientific observation. Whatever can be psychologically objectivised by the will is not the will itself, but belongs already to its incipient realization—and between this and the will itself Kant makes an explicit distinction. This incipient realization includes especially those pictures of the future, accompanied by a lively sense of values, which fill the imagination—those plans and aspirations, those complexes of the individual and collective subconscious. All these are not the will itself but the objective expression and product of the will, in which the conflict is revealed between the volitional I and the volitional Thou, first of all in psychological activity before it is converted into action on the physical plane. The will itself transcends three-dimensional space and the uni-dimensional objective flow of time. This supra-spatiality of the will can be recognized especially in the fact that in many cases one and the same will can gain possession of different human bodies which are spatially located far apart from one another and can use them as its instruments with demonic force. We shall see later the importance which all these fundamental facts have for the discussion between faith and natural science.

7. THE OBJECTIVE WORLD AS THE MEDIUM BETWEEN THE I AND THE THOU

We have been speaking so far of the two realities which we cannot observe objectively and which are consequently beyond the range of scientific investigation, the cognitive and volitional I and the cognitive and volitional Thou. Now side by side with the I and the Thou there is always also the It, the objective world towards which all the work of natural science is directed. This brings us to the question: What is the significance of the objective world within the overall picture of reality? What does it signify for the encounter between the I and the Thou? In order to answer this question we must start out from that part of the objective world which lies closest to us and which in all circumstances is the most important for our communications with each other, namely from our human bodies. My body and the body of a fellow human being, with whom I have at this particular moment to deal, form indeed only an infinitesimally small section of the immensely rich objective world which discloses itself to our eyes and which surrounds us on all sides, from the grain of sand crushed beneath our feet up to the spiral nebulae in the night sky which allow us a glimpse of distant stellar regions. In the midst of this immense objective world there stands the body of my fellow human being, speaking to me and perhaps trying to win me over for his projects. His words, which are accompanied by lively gesticulations, reveal to me first of all a new objective world which I did not know before, the world in which this other man lives, the world as it appears from his angle. His vivid words make me forget completely for a time that this world of his into which I believe I am looking is in truth only a picture of my own imagining which I am building up simply by inferring from the other man's 'outer picture' to his 'inner picture'. Indeed I do not even know whether the other man, being colour-blind perhaps and unable to distinguish red from green, actually means something totally different with his vivid description of a spring-time meadow from what his words lead me to imagine. Behind this objective world, in the narrow sense of the term, which I first perceive here, containing everything which is also contained in my own world, from the grain of sand at my feet up to the starry skies, but merely in another light and from another angle, there is still a second world belonging to the other man, a world which I must infer from his words and gestures and which is not necessarily at all the same as my own, so that it is even more difficult for me to get the feel of it and to attune my thinking to it. This is his inner, mental objective world, this inexhaustible field of study for the psychologist, which is still from the point of view of the ego just as much 'outer world' as is the objective world in the narrower sense. It is his memories and dreams, his joys and sorrows, his states of exhilaration and his states of despair. In the present context we shall not examine more closely this second, deeper stratum of the inner world of the other man which I deduce from his words and gestures: For our primary

concern here is solely with the significance, within the framework of the overall picture of reality, of the 'outer world',
in the narrower sense of the term, from which I draw my
inferences regarding the other man's 'inner picture'. This
outer world has a different look for each of the two people
whom we are for the present considering, for you and for me
in our present conversation. By making inferences from
what you say, I can establish more or less certainly how the
outer world looks from your standpoint. And yet we are both
convinced, or at least we always assume, that your world and
my world are the same world. The same world presents a
different aspect to each of us. Each of us sees it from a different angle. Neither of us has direct access to the other one's
view of the world. Neither of us can see directly into the
world-picture of the other and test the extent to which the
world-picture of the other agrees with his own or deviates
from it. Yet by means of words it is always possible to make
ourselves understood to each other, though always with the
proviso that misinterpretations may occur. It is not possible,
in doing this, to establish what the objective world is like *in
itself,* that is to say the world apart from the various aspects
of it which arise when it is viewed from various standpoints.
For in order to establish what the 'world in itself' looks like, I
should need to envisage it as the object of my investigation,
and it would thus still not be the world as it is 'in itself' but
the world as it represents itself to me. Kant applied the term
'thing in itself' (*das Ding an sich*) to this unknown quantity
in which the whole relation between subject and object is
eliminated. But this thing in itself is in our thinking never
more than a peripheral concept, an unknown quantity, an x
shrouded in total obscurity. We can assert neither a positive
nor a negative proposition about it. We can say neither that
it exists nor that it does not exist; for as soon as we do that, as
soon as we form any conception of it, indeed as soon as we
speak of it at all, we have thereby already made an object of
it and consequently tacitly presupposed a subject of whose
world-outlook it forms a part. Thus we can never do otherwise than pass over the 'thing in itself' in silence. The
objective world, of which alone we can talk together, is what

lies as a unity beneath the multiplicity of aspects which the world presents in the consciousness of the many subjects who regard it, the one primordial riddle which is always mirrored from a new angle in each of the countless subjects whose organs of sense are directed towards it. In every act of scientific observation upon which we human beings are able to agree, we must still bear in mind this insuperable barrier, deriving from the structure of reality, which limits the scope of all our knowing.

After these preliminary remarks we can form a clear notion of the position which the objective world, the sole object of all scientific investigation, occupies within the framework of reality as a whole. Let us confine our study for the moment to the two people who confront one another as the I and the Thou. If we assume them to be alone together in the world, then the two parts of the world of objects with which the two of us, you and I, are continually concerned are the two bodies whose utterances we both perceive, my body and your body on whose movements all our mutual understanding and combined activity depend. These two bodies confront both of us as objects. Even my body, as Rickert has emphasized in his book, *The Object of Knowledge,*[1] belongs just as much as does the rest of the world of objects, to the objective world outside. Your body as I see it belongs to my objective world; and my body as you see it occupies a place in your objective world. This part of the objective world, with which we both continually have to deal in communicating with each other, resembles an opaque wall separating two cells in a prison. Neither of the two prisoners can see into the other one's cell. Neither knows what the inside of the other's cell looks like. And so each one sees only one side even of the party-wall which separates the two cells. And yet it is one and the same wall and is part of both cells, even though it presents a different side to each of the two prisoners. It is because of this that the party-wall serves the two lonely captives as an invaluable medium for communicating with each other. It enables them to make themselves understood to each other by knocking on it with an ever more highly developed sign-language.

---

[1] *Der Gegenstand der Erkenntnis.*

This party-wall furnishes a graphic analogy for the significance of the objective world within the structure of reality as
a whole.

In order to make clear all the relations which are transmitted through this medium, we must now modify and extend
our analogy somewhat. We will suppose that the medium
through which the two persons can establish communication
with each other does not consist of solid material, as did the
wall between the two prison cells which could therefore trans-
mit only the sound of knocks, but of a soft mass of wax, opaque
but so thin that I can produce in it with my finger an 'impression' (in the literal sense of the word) which then becomes
visible in the next cell as a corresponding 'expression'. This
gives us a fairly apposite analogy for the significance of the
objective world first of all for the relation between the I and
the Thou. Whatever influences I may receive from you,
whether you play a Mozart sonata to me or embrace me or box
my ears or knock me down in a violent scuffle, all these are
nothing but various 'expressions' which become visible and
palpable on the waxen wall of the cell of my objective space
and which you produce as the corresponding 'impressions' on
your side of the wall, within your cell into which, of course, I
cannot see. I reciprocate the effects which you evoke in this
way in my objective space with corresponding counter-effects
which I bring to bear on the cell wall between us. Throughout this interplay of effects and counter-effects neither of us
can see into the inner world of the other. I do not know the
motives for the unkind words you address to me, and you do
not know how deeply I have been wounded by certain things
you have said. Everything which takes place between us is
then, to quote Jaspers once more, an encounter between two
'lonely souls' which remain alone even when they are engaged
in the most impassioned conflict with one another. The
encounter always takes place through the medium of the
objective world, which we can affect, each from our own side.
This objective world is the instrument on which we both play
and which serves us as an invaluable means of expression.

In all this we have so far dealt only with the relation between two persons, confronting one another as the I and the

Thou. But there exist not only these two human bodies which we took as our starting-point. We are standing in the midst of an unobservable space, encompassing the whole of reality, a space in which, behind the objective forms which alone are visible, there stand an immense and innumerable multitude of subjects, infinitesimally few of which are known to us, and each of them is continually encountering others. Let us consider the psychical substratum of the entire world of animals and plants and beyond it the unplumbed depths of inorganic reality with its mysterious life of which we are learning more and more through the discoveries of contemporary atomic physics. For all the subjects, invisible to us, which may stand concealed behind the objective world, this objective world is itself the medium which makes possible the encounters that take place between them. This renders the picture by which we have represented objective space considerably more complicated than was at first necessary; for now there are no longer just two solitary prisoners who can communicate with each other through the thin but completely opaque wall that separates their cells. The number of solitary prisoners has now enormously increased. And yet it is still one and the same party-wall which forms the medium, common to them all, through which they affect one another. Naturally, not every subject which is part of the cosmos affects every other subject; and these encounters may assume the most extremely varied forms, of which only very few are known to us from our limited human experience. Yet for all the encounters which take place between the most varying subjects and in the most varying forms, the objective world-space is always the common medium through which they are transmitted. Each subject perceives this objective world always from the side which it presents to him, while the view which all the others have of the world remains unknown to him. The objective world as a whole is thus the totality of all the views of it of all the subjects in the cosmos. It is the world as it displays itself at each moment simultaneously in all its aspects. The relation between the two sides of one and the same party-wall has now become a relation between innumerable sides of one and the same medium. A wall which

possesses simultaneously an infinite number of sides is not a
possible conception for our human imagination. Yet we do
possess an obscure sense of the infinite depth, wealth and
variety of the world to which we belong.

With all this we have still not dealt with the full significance of the objective world, this medium in which the
encounters between subjects take place. We must end this
chapter by adverting to one further important point which
has not yet been mentioned. The objective world, as we have
seen, is not merely the object of our knowledge but first and
foremost the instrument of our activity, the tool with which
each one of us, at the position in the front line which has been
assigned to him, participates in the work of determining the
future configuration of the world. But, as was shown in the
first volume of this work,[1] reality confronts us objectively only
when it has passed from the molten state of becoming into the
solid state of having become. 'Whatever is becoming first
leaps, as it were, into the space of the available (*vorhanden*)
time continuum; with and in this leap this space is continually
renewed; and whatever becomes occupies a definite position
within it.'[2] The 'impression' which I within my cell produce
on the soft partition wall which stands between us as medium,
whether it consists in a word I address to you or in a blow I
deliver you or in a generous outstretching of my hand to take
you up lovingly by the arm, this impression will never become
an 'expression', objectively perceptible in your cell, until
after it has become an accomplished fact. It is just the same
in the converse case, when the 'impression' which you produce on the cell wall on your side becomes in my cell the
'expression' of the spirit and the direction in which you are
working, at your allotted place in the front line, in helping
to shape the future of the world. Thus it is always only
through the medium of the having-become, of the objectively
solidified, that the two of us can converse together and make
ourselves understood.

This brings us to the question whether there is not also a
relation between the I and the Thou which is 'still on this

---

[1] *Glaube und Denken*, 4, (*Belief and Thought*), p. 110ff.
[2] *loc. cit.* pp. 107-8.

side' of this objective solidification. If we human beings were merely objective structures, that possibility would be excluded from the outset. We could then only bump together on the objective plane like the balls on a billiard table and so impart a new direction to each other. But in fact we two, the I and the Thou, in the depths of our being, are situated in the non-objective space. A relation is therefore possible between us which arises already at the stage at which the objective solidification has not yet taken place at all, in other words in the molten state of becoming in which events have not yet assumed a solid form. Since the two of us, each from his own allotted station and each working in a definite direction, are collaborating in determining the future configuration of the world, our collaboration too and our mutual opposition must at every moment anew pass through this molten state. The relation in which we stand to one another in this undecided state of becoming, out of which the ensuing cosmic instant is born, cannot be objectively expressed at all. It has not yet been projected onto the three-dimensional physical space. It is something totally unobservable. And yet we all have immediate knowledge of this unobservable relation. It is quite as familiar to us as our own unobjectivised ego, which indeed, as Rickert says, is more immediately familiar to us than is the entire objective world around us, although we cannot envisage it as an object because it is too close to us to confront us as something visible. We stand in this mysterious relation to one another even within the state of becoming through which reality passes before it solidifies into what has become. We are aware of one another and encounter one another even before this encounter has assumed an objective form. This unobservable contact may be a passionate inner conflict, an almost unbearable tension, if the directions in which the two of us would like to mould the world are opposed. But this relation may also be an inward harmony, a community of purpose, which is essentially already present even before it has acquired an objective form, before any word has been spoken and before any deed has been done. It is also possible, however, and this will usually be the case, that this invisible relation swings to and fro between the two

opposite poles. The conflict between the I and the Thou and
the support which they afford one another, all still 'on this
side' of objectivity—these are the hidden fountainhead from
which the river of world history flows, the dark womb of which
world events are born.

Our human encounter with the Thou is, as we have seen,
simply the special form of the encounter of which we, con-
versing here, have immediate knowledge. But it is permissible
for us to suppose that the whole of reality is a world of
encounters in which this underlying theme recurs in an
infinite number of modifications and variations. The region
of these encounters, of which in our human sphere we see
only a limited section, is a space comprising the whole of
reality. If that is the case, then what we have had to say
about the relation between the I and the Thou, as a relation
prior to the objective solidification, applies not only to the
human sphere but to the whole of reality. This relation of
conflict and mutual assistance may arise between us and any
other beings which are involved together in the tremendous
process of becoming, out of which, from one cosmic instant
to the next, the future of the world is born. That is why
since the earliest times, side by side with the technical influencing of nature, and indeed long before that was achieved,
there has always been a magical relation with world events.
The technical intellect approaches nature as an observer and
looks at it objectively from outside in order to establish
empirically the laws according to which it functions and then,
on the basis of this experience, to direct it according to his
will. The man of magic, on the other hand, acts on the basis
of an immediate natural affinity, an inner oneness with nature,
without conscious reflection. It is evident that all the magical
rites and incantations with which primitive man sought to
acquire power over nature, that is to say the whole of white
magic and black magic, derive ultimately from this same
instinctively clairvoyant affinity with nature.

We in this age of technology regard it as meaningless super-
stition or ridiculous nonsense if the governor of a Chinese
province after the execution of a famous robber chieftain
drains off the dead man's blood and drinks it in order to

appropriate to himself the boldness and courage of this dangerous brigand,[1] or if the antelope hunters of a certain African
tribe, at sunrise on a day when there is to be a hunt, pierce
the image of an antelope with their spears, invoking the sun
and performing various solemn ceremonies, in order to be
sure of catching their quarry. But this superficial judgment
passed by modern ' enlightened ' man shows only that he has
lost an entire sense, so that he can no longer at all understand
the significance of these ancient magical customs. The magic
of the man of nature cannot be approached with rational
thought. The objective thinking of the intellectual never
discerns more than the outward performance of these peculiar
customs, the eating of the ashes of burnt hairs amongst the
chamois hunters of the Tyrol, the blowing in the faces of sick
people in order to fill them with healthy psychical material by
breath magic, or the drinking of the blood of slain enemies.
But the magical power of these customs does not reside at all
in the outward and visible actions as such. The deep underlying meaning of all magic, concealed behind this strange and
gruesome outward appearance, becomes clear to us only if we
understand something which has been said by Dacqué, following up Schopenhauer's treatise and Schertel's work on the
subject. 'In all accounts of genuinely magical activity the
central feature of the action is the complete self-abandonment
of the agent to his task, to his magical purpose, even at the cost
of his life. You must give yourself up to the forces of nature
with your blood, your vital fluid, your very essence. You must
immolate your soul, and not wish to retain it, if you would
achieve the true magical effect. . . . The idea of the death of
the soul, of sacrifice, stands as the vital force at the centre of
all magic. Wherever consciously personal life is not offered
up, no true magic is possible, be it white magic or black.'[2]
That is why in uncivilized communities the central ceremony
of the magic rite can be performed only in a state of ecstasy,
so that the performer abandons himself completely and loses
all personal consciousness. According to Schertel's work, this

[1] Johannes Warneck, *Die Lebenskräfte des Evangeliums in der animistischen Heidenwelt* (*The Vital Forces of the Gospel in the World of Animistic Paganism*), p. 44.
[2] Edgar Dacqué, *Natur und Seele* (*Nature and Soul*), p. 80.

giving up of one's own existence is also the ultimate meaning
of the sacrifice in all religions. 'Its meaning does not consist
merely in "presenting" various things to the demon in order
to put it in a favourable mood; its essential significance lies in
the mystical union with the demon itself.' In his latest book,
Paradise Lost, Dacqué says in this connexion: 'To stand
within the magical relation and to engage in magical activity
is extremely dangerous and arduous and demands that the
agent should devote his entire physical and mental energy to
it; it overwhelms both the performer himself and the partici-
pants who are more or less actively involved.'[1] 'Behind all
genuinely magical, i.e. all genuinely pagan life and activity
there again and again stands death. In other words there lie behind it the entire primordial foundations of life, of existence.'[2]

We shall have to return to magic in another connexion,
namely in discussing the question of the relationship between
belief in miracles and the granting of prayers on the one hand
and the scientific conception of the universe on the other. In
the present context it was necessary only to show in principle
why it is that, even in the midst of the age of technology which
began its triumphal progress when civilized man first limited
his horizon to the space of the objective world, the primeval
'magical man' still re-emerges from the depths, though in a
new form, and, as a necessary reaction against the uninspiring
spirit of technology, the notion of influencing the world by
magic continually reasserts itself. The reason for this is that
the ubiquitous medium which serves as an intermediary in
all encounters between the I and the Thou, before entering
the solidified state of objectivity, first always passes through the
molten state of becoming, and that we ourselves as non-
objective subjects are able to enter into a mysterious relation,
already at this stage of becoming, with the psychical substrata
of cosmic events, of which we are directly aware in our struggle
to decide the future.

[1] Edgar Dacqué, *Das verlorene Paradies*, Munich and Berlin, 1938, p. 284.
[2] *Ibid.*, p. 294.

F

8. THE PROBLEM OF THE PSYCHICAL CONTENT
OF THE WORLD

In the previous chapter it was seen that the objective world is the medium through which the I and the Thou become perceptible to each other and are enabled to affect each other. This is true first of all within the human sphere; but, as we have seen, we cannot help suspecting that it applies not only to relations between one human being and another but also to the relation between man and the rest of nature. The primeval magical man tries to place himself in intimate contact with the psychical substrata of natural processes outside the human sphere in order to make the natural forces subservient to his purposes. We must reckon with the possibility that the 'medial' significance of the objective world does not apply only to the relation between one human being and another and to the relation between man and non-human nature, but that even within the world of non-human nature itself there may exist psychical relations which do not differ essentially, even though they may have quite another form, from what we ourselves experience in our own human sphere as the encounter between the I and the Thou. We cannot help thinking that the whole of reality around us is not simply an inanimate mass, but that there lies behind it something which presents an analogy, however distant, with what we call a Thou. This raises the ancient question which has occupied men's minds for thousands of years, the question whether perhaps the whole world is animate. If we bring up this question as part of the groundwork for a discussion between belief and natural science, we do not do so out of a poetical desire to project into nature with fancy-free enthusiasm our human feelings, our sorrows and joys, nor yet out of idle speculativeness. We are concerned rather with forming a comprehensive picture of reality. We are asking what, within the framework of this comprehensive picture, is the significance of the objective world with which natural science concerns itself, and what is the relation between this objective world and the non-objective realities of which we possess immediate knowledge. In the course of this investigation, therefore, we approach the

problem of the psychical content of the world as a matter for
sober observation. We are seeking to establish what indications we can derive from observation of the world of experience which will help us to answer this question, and where the
limits lie beyond which we can never hope to advance in our
researches. Here again, therefore, we must first set out from
our human field of experience, which alone is immediately
accessible to us, and then ask whether and to what extent this
human experience leads us to conclusions and analogical
inferences which point the way beyond its own boundaries.

Amongst modern scientists it is Eddington who has pointed
out with particular emphasis that our own ego is the only place
where we can see immediately, from within, the reality which
everywhere else only appears to us from without. Eddington
speaks of the 'direct insight which we possess in our own
consciousness . . . into the cosmic basis behind the symbols'.
'I have immediate knowledge of being, because I myself am,
and I have immediate knowledge of becoming, because I myself become. It is, so to speak, the essential ego of all that is
and is becoming.' 'We must remember that the physical
world of atoms, electrons and quanta is the abstract, symbolical
representation of a something. In general we know nothing
of what lies behind the symbols; we do not know the inner
essence of that which we designate with these symbols. But
there is one point of contact of the physical world with consciousness at which we do become acquainted with the conscious essentiality. This is the self or mind, of which the
physical image and symbol is the brain cell.' In all observations of this kind a clear distinction is drawn between the
immediate insight into reality which I possess at the one point
where I myself am collaborating, with my being, in the becoming of the world and the indirect, secondhand relation in
which I stand to all the rest of reality. There is only one place
where I have an 'inner picture' of reality. Of everything
else I receive only the objective 'outer picture', even when I
penetrate into the world of the electrons with the help of the
most powerful ultra-microscopes and by means of the most
precise spectroscopic observation of their wave-frequencies.
Even when I apply the most exact methods, I achieve only an

'abstract, symbolical representation of a something', the innermost essence of which I can never fathom.

If we wish to discuss the proper significance of objective knowledge within the framework of our entire conception of reality, we must first of all start out from the distinction which Eddington and other physicists have drawn between the 'inner picture' and the 'outer picture'. The difference between these two aspects becomes clearest to me in my relation with 'my' own body. I can look at my body from outside. I can look at it in the mirror, in order to have the view of it which other people receive who look at it from without. If I happen to be a doctor or a scientist myself, I can examine parts of my body anatomically. I can carry out a blood test and subject the specimen to chemical analysis. I can X-ray my lung and so arrive at the most exact possible diagnosis. In all this I am always concerned solely with forming an 'outside picture'. I join in the work of examining my body, but, in general, other people, and particularly specialists, who can look closely at every part of it under the magnifying glass as disinterested spectators, are far better qualified for this than I am. But this forming of an 'outer picture' of me reaches a quite definite limit at which the competence of my fellow human beings ceases, no matter how earnestly they may strive to advance further. There is an innermost area to which I myself alone have direct access, and into which nobody else can look. I alone know what I suffer and what joys I experience. Others may endeavour, by means of their imagination, to put themselves in my place and to share in my joys and sorrows. Yet anyone who does not know from his own experience the pangs of hunger, for example, or what it means to have toothache or migraine, can indeed very accurately analyse the nervous disturbances which these pains cause, but he has no knowledge whatsoever of the 'inside picture' of these processes. None of us can look directly into the sphere of consciousness of another. Nor can I see into the world-picture in which reality is mirrored in your consciousness, and, what constitutes a still greater obstacle to mutual comprehension, I cannot see even into the memories, conceptions and thoughts which arise in your mind or into the joys which exalt your soul, or the pains which inwardly torment and convulse you. The command 'Rejoice with them that do rejoice, and weep with them that weep' can therefore always be only approximately fulfilled, even amongst those who possess a great gift of empathy. For my consciousness and your consciousness are not like two adjoining rooms, connected by a door which can at any time be opened. Neither of us can disclose himself directly to the other. Because this is so, any mutual exchange, any sharing in the destiny of another, even between people who are inwardly very close to one another, can always take place only by indirect means, namely through the continual conscious or unconscious drawing of analogical inferences on the basis of long experience. When the other person laughs or weeps, turns pale or blushes, and especially when he speaks to me and tells me about his state of mind, I infer from this that behind these movements and alterations in the appearance of his face, and especially behind the words that issue from his mouth, there lie the same inner experiences and disturbances which are taking place in me myself when my body utters similar sounds and executes corresponding movements. In all this, then, I clearly distinguish the 'outer picture' of reality, the manifestations of life which are visible and audible from without, and which are all that I can perceive in any of my fellow human beings, even in my most intimate friends, from the 'inside picture' of what is going on, of which I have a direct view only in my own self.

Why is that so? We are confronted here with the important consequence which follows from the fact of which the fundamental significance has become clear to us in the preceding chapters. We spoke there of the relation in which my destiny links me, a supra-spatial ego, to the particular structure in the objective world which I call 'my' body, so that 'my' body's destiny is 'my' destiny. From this irrevocable attachment, it follows that the struggle which this physical organism wages for its existence against forces that are endeavouring to injure and destroy it is 'my' struggle. All other people, however attentively they may follow this struggle, are at best sympathetic spectators or war correspondents and have only an 'outside picture' of the battle. But I myself feel every attack to which this body is exposed in its struggle for existence as a blow aimed directly against me myself. I cannot regard it from the point of view of a neutral spectator. I must defend myself against it and go over to the offensive with a counter-attack. The clash which necessarily ensues in this conflict is suffering. The pain that suddenly arises at some part of my body which is in danger may be compared with an alarm which is sounded in a besieged fortress at the place where the enemy has breached the wall and which summons all available forces to hasten to meet the threat. I suffer in the battle with deadly forces which menace my body, and my whole body is pervaded with the joy of living when the attack is victoriously beaten off, when I have been faint and weary and a cooling drink slakes my thirst, or when after a severe illness the morbid substances are expelled in a crisis of fever and my recovery begins. In pain and joy alike, then, at the particular point to which I am bound by my destiny, I participate directly in the experience of the coming into being, the becoming, of the ensuing cosmic instant, just as a soldier, at the particular point in the line to which he personally is assigned, experiences directly the gigantic conflict in which his nation is struggling, on a long front, for a new configuration of the world, while he receives news of all the other operations only indirectly through the reports of war correspondents and can thus form only an 'outside picture' of what is happening.

It is of crucial importance for our whole understanding of nature, including even the underlying concepts of contemporary physics, that we do not have only the objective 'outside picture' of the particular physical structure we call our body, but that we are obliged to share directly, trembling and rejoicing, despairing and then breathing freely again, in the experience of every vicissitude in the course of the long and complicated war of attrition which this one particular organism has to fight out against a thousand enemies on innumerable fronts, until at last, exhausted after decades of heroic resistance, it succumbs to the superior power of its adversaries. And so at this one point we see the world not from one side only but always from two sides at once. We see it simultaneously from within and from without and we can compare the two views and establish what 'inside picture' corresponds to what 'outside picture'. The fact that at this one point we possess a double picture of reality is of inestimable value for our whole understanding of nature, since the self-observation which is possible for us at this point is the basis upon which we can draw the most important conclusions about the hidden inner world which in all other fields of reality lies concealed behind the visible façade. Now, all the conclusions which we draw on this basis are analogical inferences. For they are founded on the assumption, which suggests itself to us quite involuntarily, that if in the objective world around me I encounter any phenomenon which resembles the 'outside picture' of my own body, then the 'inner picture' also, which lies hidden behind this exterior, will resemble the 'inner picture which lies hidden behind my body and about which I alone have immediate knowledge. This well-known analogical inference underlies in the first place everything which, in our everyday intercourse with our fellow human beings, we learn about their hidden inner life, with its passions and emotions, from the movements they make, the cries of joy and pain they utter, and the changing expressions on their faces. The further we carry our self-observation, the greater is our 'knowledge of human nature'; for this is precisely the ability to deduce from the 'utterances' of others, on the basis of our own self-knowledge, what it is that is happening within them, corresponding to this 'outer picture'.

This analogical inference from the visible objective picture to the invisible inner being is by no means confined to our relations with those of our fellow creatures which stand closest to us and which we can therefore most easily understand, namely our fellow human beings. We involuntarily extend this inferential procedure to include other beings, which are further removed from us but with which we still possess a certain similarity. These are in the first place the higher mammals, whose nervous system, bone structure, blood circulation, hearts, respiratory organs and digestive apparatus closely resemble our own. But we cannot limit ourselves, in drawing these inferences, to the animals which are close to us; whether we like it or not, we must extend the procedure to include all the rest of the animal world, not excepting the birds, insects and worms and even the simplest bacteria and bacilli which at first sight seem to have no more in common with us than the fact that they too seek nourishment, defend themselves and reproduce. When the drones soar up from the beehive into the blue sky on their marriage and death flight, when a fly is caught in the web and struggles desperately to escape the threads in which the spider has enmeshed it, when chickens crowd together trembling while the goshawk circles above them, or when the father lion plays tenderly with his cubs, then we suspect that behind all these various sounds and movements there lie fears, desires and erotic passions such as we know from our inner life.

Once we have extended this analogical inference to cover the most rudimentary beings at the lowest limits of animal life, once we say with Schiller that 'worms too are voluptuaries', then we cannot stop short of the vegetable kingdom. Here indeed we are venturing into a field where we are not always standing on very firm ground. We are fully aware that we are in danger of making fantastic conjectures. Yet from a simple animal, for example a polyp which sits in one place on the floor of the ocean and uses its arms to catch its prey and push it into its alimentary canal, it is only a short step to a plant. The plant too takes its nourishment from its environment, defends itself in many cases against its enemies with dangerous weapons such as thorns and barbs—consider the cruel prickles with which the cacti in the desert ward off the thirsty animals which roam the wastes—and has a highly developed sexual life with male and female organs. These same organic processes, which in the case of even the simplest animal we suppose to reflect a rich and eventful inner life, with joys, pains and all kinds of emotional disturbances, are they then in the case of the plant a mere inanimate mechanism? The growth of flowers has been filmed and it has been shown that if we look at the development of a flowering plant through the time-lens, reducing each day to one second, then the process is reminiscent of the respiratory movements of a human being. If we film with the same chronological foreshortening a creeper climbing up a wall and then over on to a pole into which it can sink its roots, we cannot resist the impression that this plant is moving like a man who stretches out his arms into the void, trembling, seeking and groping, and then, when he has at last found the hold he so intensely longs for, grasps it for all he is worth, as a drowning man grasps a rescuing plank and lies clinging to it with immense relief. If we do not involuntarily attribute to the plant a similar inner life to that which we take for granted in the case of even the simpler animals, that is obviously entirely due to the fact that the plant has a much slower tempo than we fast-living human beings have, so that the drawing of a single breath occupies as long a time in the life of a plant as a whole day does in the life of a man. But after all, the measurement of time is something quite relative. In one hour one can see under the microscope many generations of bacteria coming into being and reproducing by cell division. Obviously these tiny beings have a very much quicker tempo than we have. The life of a generation, which for us occupies thirty years, for them lasts only a minute. While the bacteria live more rapidly than we do, the plant obviously lives far more slowly. That is why the life of flowers, shrubs and trees at first sight appears to us as static and inanimate, a 'vegetating', 'a twilight existence', while perhaps in fact it is accompanied by inward disturbances just as intense as those which accompany the lives of human beings and animals.

The inferential procedure which leads us to an inner world behind the 'outward picture' of our natural environment has now been followed through from man by way of the mammals to the bacteria and from the bacteria on to the plants. We have seen that this procedure is entirely dependent upon the position from which it is undertaken and which forms the basis for all the analogies which lead us to these inferences. We draw our inferences always from the standpoint of man. For our human inner life, or strictly speaking my own inner life, is the only one I know, since it is only at this point that I see the world from both sides and am able to discern the connexion between the 'inner picture' and the 'outer picture'. This human inner life is the only sure foundation upon which to build up the whole structure of analogical inferences. The procedure followed in this construction may be summarized in the following rule: the more closely any structure in the world around me resembles my human body in its organization and expressions, the more indications I shall have upon which to base my analogical inferences and the fuller will be the picture which I form of its inner life. Conversely, the less closely such a structure resembles my body, the fainter and vaguer its 'inner picture' will become for me, and the more its inner life will appear to me as a soulless sleep or semi-animate twilight. It is quite impossible for us to avoid employing this method in making our inferences about the psychical condition of our fellow creatures. This inferential procedure forces itself upon us directly. And yet we must frankly admit that if we consider this method of investigation from the scientific point of view it appears to us to be extraordinarily questionable. It is just as one-sided and naïvely anthropocentric as was the opinion of the ancient Greeks that the other nations, who did not speak Greek, had no language at all but were βάρβαροι, that is to say people who utter only meaningless and inarticulate sounds. If we imagine for a moment that some other beings, for example fish, were in a position to form conjectures regarding our human inner life, then this method would presumably lead them to suppose that we human beings, whose movements are so entirely different from theirs and who cannot even draw a single breath in that universal provider and home, the vital element, water, without immediately dying, must surely possess only a very low degree of animation. From all this we can see that it is by no means an objective, scientific assertion, but an entirely subjective, human point of view, when we assume that the inner life has reached a maximum level only in man, and that it decreases more and more and approaches a minimum level the further removed from man the natural beings are in their shape and organization, until it finally vanishes in obscurity entirely when we reach the world of plants. Looking at it objectively, it is, to say the least, more probable that all natural structures alike possess a psychical substratum, but that other beings, which differ from us outwardly, are also inwardly otherwise constituted than ourselves, and that consequently the inner life of, say, a plant is so extremely different from our own soul-life that out of our limited human experience we can form no conception of it whatever.

This brings us to a question which has necessarily to be raised in this context because it is of decisive significance for our whole understanding of nature, the question whether it is permissible for us to restrict 'natural animation' to the organic world. Does it then extend only as far as the simplest organisms, for example the single-cell plant? Or must we reckon with the possibility that behind inorganic nature too there is something which in some way resembles our own soul-life? If there were any objective justification for the analogical inference whereby we make similarity to mankind the criterion by which we establish the presence of psychical life, then it would be reasonable for us to say that, if in the plant we find only a vegetative twilight condition since all it has in common with humanity is that it feeds, defends and reproduces itself, then even this minimum of animate life is obviously entirely absent when we pass on from organic to inorganic nature. For an inorganic structure, a crystal or a star or an atom, already presents no analogy whatsoever with us human beings. But once we have understood how biased and dubious this anthropocentric reasoning is, we shall see that one would be jumping to a quite unwarranted conclusion if one were to assume that the wonderful structures of the inorganic world possess only an objective façade but no psychical substratum. It is not only poetic and imaginative personalities like Giordano Bruno who have been unable to tolerate the thought that the whole immense might of nature is shrouded in the night of unconsciousness and that the light of consciousness has flashed out only at the few points on the earth's crust where organic life has come into being, or in other words that the world of consciousness consists only of single widely scattered sparks of light which for a moment faintly illumine their surroundings amidst the immense cosmic obscurity and then sink back again into the everlasting night of unconsciousness. It is significant that even strict and exact natural scientists have, on the basis of their observations, rejected this so-called 'night view'. The astronomer Kepler in his book, *De Harmonice mundi*, expressed the view that the earth is not a lifeless mass but an animate being 'which with the rise and fall of its breathing, its periodical sleeping and waking dependent upon the sun, causes the flow and ebb of the ocean tides'.

In more recent times Ernst Haeckel as a biologist has defended the theory of the animate nature of atoms. The problem of the animation of plants has been most thoroughly investigated by Gustav Theodor Fechner,[1] who was originally a student of medicine and subsequently became the founder of what is described as 'experimental psychology' and discovered the so-called Weber-Fechner law. In his principal work, *Zend-Avesta*,[2] he made a thorough study of the animation of inorganic structures, particularly of the stars and planets. This led him to the idea of extending one step further the analogical argument by which he had arrived at the animation of plants, and maintaining that the earth itself is an animate, self-moving organism. For just as in the case of man the firm skeletal structure actuates and organizes the periodical oscillations of the movable components, i.e. the muscular movements, the rhythm of the circulation of the blood, respiration and the metabolism, so in the case of the earth also there is a solid framework which actuates and organizes the play of moving components. These movable parts are, first of all, the principal ocean currents, the tides, the rivers and winds, the seasons of the day and the year. The earth, too, like our bodies, 'has at a certain time been born out of a greater material sphere of which it was once a part'. 'The earth, like man, interacts with an exterior world and is subject both in its outward movements and in its inward processes to the influence of this outer world; but just as man differentiates himself from other terrestrial creatures, so the earth too differentiates itself from other celestial bodies as a being with an individual nature of its own, partly through the peculiar way in which it combines and realizes its inner

[1] G. T. Fechner, *Nanna, die Beseelung der Pflanzen (Nanna or the Animation of Plants)*, Leipzig, 1848.
[2] G. T. Fechner, *Zend-Avesta*, Leipzig, 1851. Vol. I, p. 30.

processes and partly through the manner in which it reacts against external influences.' Fechner thinks that if we could observe on a reduced scale, perhaps in a retort, the efficient movement which the earth performs around its mother the sun in order to receive nourishment from it through the receptive organs which it turns towards it before converting this nourishment into organic vital processes, then any zoologically trained observer would immediately be driven to the conclusion that this spherical being must be a living organism. He would note only that in this organism, in accordance with its peculiar alimentary system, the skeletal structure does not surround the internal organs as a protective armour, as ours does, but that it forms the solid inner nucleus, while the more delicate organs, which absorb and chemically elaborate its nourishment, are turned outwards.

There is no occasion for us now to examine more closely Fechner's bold comparison of the stars and planets with earthly organisms or to test its validity. For in attempting, as we are now doing, to extend the psychical content of the world beyond the boundaries of organic nature, we are not in the first place thinking of such massive structures as the stars. We are much more closely concerned at present with the world of the tiniest components of reality, the molecules, atoms, protons and electrons. For these are for us no longer merely lifeless little lumps of building material, but systems with an intense inner motive force, their smallest particles in a state of periodical oscillation which preserves the equilibrium of the whole, just as the stability of a swarm of bees is maintained from within by the presence of the queen. If we look, for example, at a greatly enlarged instantaneous picture of the path which a sheaf of X-rays takes through the air and if we observe how the electrons (beta particles) knocked out of the molecules of air fly out in all directions, we are reminded of a flock of migratory birds at which a shot has been fired fluttering away in all directions in terror. Marie Curie was once moved by her new discovery to say: 'Seemingly rigid material is the scene of births, murderous clashes and acts of self-annihilation. It is the scene of life and death.' And the physicist Hermann Weyl says: 'It follows that the material particle is itself not even a point in the electrical space. It is not spatial—extensive—at all. But it is situated in a spatial environment which forms the starting-point for its electrical actions. In this it is analogous to the ego, for although the ego is itself non-spatial, its actions arise through its body always at a definite position in the cosmic continuum. Whatever this energizing agent may be in its inner essence—perhaps life and will—we regard it in physics only in terms of the actions it provokes and it is only by virtue of these actions that we are able to characterize it numerically.'[1]

It is a step of fundamental importance for the understanding of the whole reality of which we are parts, when sober natural scientists, not on the basis of any idle speculation but under the impulsion of the facts they have observed, are driven to the conclusion that not only organic structures but even inorganic processes possibly conceal something which, even though only in a very figurative sense, is 'analogous to the ego' or 'perhaps life and will'. We may of course reject from the outset as mere speculative fancy the notion that even outside the world of animals, which have a bodily structure closely related to our own, there might be something presenting even the most distant analogy with what, in the human sphere, we call 'life and will'. We may take the view that it is not at all permissible for us in this question to leave the solid ground of verified experience. But if we really want to keep to the facts which are accessible to experimental observation, then strictly speaking we ought not to make any kind of assertions at all even about the inner life of animals. We may, like Descartes, regard them merely as soulless mechanisms, for, after all, animals cannot converse with us, so that we cannot ask them whether our conjectures about their inner life are correct or whether we have merely read into them our own human feelings and psychological processes.[2] Consequently there is here no control or experimental

---

[1] Hermann Weyl, *Was ist Materie?* (*What is Matter?*), 1924, p. 58.
[2] A direct interrogation of animals is certainly possible if Paula Moekel's reports about her dog Rolf turn out to be true. They are communicated, together with the names of witnesses in her two books, *Erinnerungen und Briefe meines Hundes Rolf* (*Memories and Letters of my Dog Rolf*), 1920, and *Mein Hund Rolf* (*My Dog Rolf*), 1921, published by Robert Lutz, Stuttgart.

verification of the correctness of our conjectures. But there is no field, not even the field of exact physics, in which we can restrict our quest for knowledge to that which can be directly observed with our organs of sense, with the help perhaps of the spectroscope and the electron microscope. We necessarily combine our observations to form thoughts and summarize them in more general formulae which go far beyond anything that can be carried out in the laboratory. Thus zoology, in its researches into animal psychology, has long since crossed the frontier which separates man and beast. And so we cannot break off our chain of reasoning even when we reach the frontier between beast and plant. For the world of animals and the world of plants overlap in certain intermediate forms. As soon as we have extended the principle of animation to the world of plants, the modern conception of the analysis of matter into periodically motivated systems of electrons brings us quite automatically to the question whether it is really conceivable that the two-sidedness of reality, the correspondence of an invisible 'inner picture' with the visible 'outer picture', suddenly ceases when we reach the limits of the organic world. Does not even the principle that *natura non facit saltus* compel us to assume from the outset that in the inorganic sphere too there lies behind the visible outer world an invisible inner region which may perhaps bear a distant likeness to the psychical life of living organisms?

And so we come to the extremely important sentences in which P. Jordan, in his book about physics and the secret of organic life, sums up the attitude to the question of the animate nature of the world which we are compelled, from the point of view of natural science, to adopt today, now that atomic physics has bridged the gap between the giant molecule and the unicellular organism. 'There has been plenty of speculation and writing about whether the lower animals, and even the plants, also possesses anything resembling a sentient soul. Unfortunately we are very far not only from being able to answer that question but even from being able to say at all exactly what it is actually intended to mean. Thus we know nothing about whether even the self-multiplying molecules perhaps possess a trace of sentience and possibly experience just a faint presentiment of the satisfaction which reproduction affords us higher animals.'[1]

We cannot rest content with these purely empirical conclusions of scientific observation, finishing by saying *ignoramus* and venturing only a few vague conjectures. We must advance a step further and ponder for another moment over the fundamental significance for our entire understanding of reality of precisely this negative or sceptical result beyond which we cannot go in this question. We have seen that our inferences from the 'outer picture' to the 'inner picture' of reality led us, within the relatively restricted field from which we began, to fairly certain conclusions. Here we were standing at a place upon which a bright light falls; but the further we moved from this brightly lighted spot, the more deeply we entered into a dense fog where we could only grope our way forward very uncertainly, saying that here there was perhaps 'something like a sensitive soul' or 'a trace of sentience' or 'a faint presentiment of the satisfaction' which we human beings experience. The brightly lighted space within which we were able to take a few fairly sure steps was the area nearest to our human existence, including the beasts which closely resemble man. The outer region, where our path is lost in night and fog and where we can hazard only very tentative estimates, was the place where the boundary becomes fluid between the simplest organisms and the molecules, which from one point of view are still within the purview of biology and from the other point of view are already nothing more than physical magnitudes. Why is it then that, as soon as we leave that innermost area, we approach more and more closely a frontier zone in which everything is lost in mist? The reason is obviously not, as we always suppose, that the thing itself which we are seeking to discover, namely the 'inner picture' of reality behind the visible 'outer picture', becomes steadily darker and weaker and dimmer as soon as we have crossed the frontier of our immediate environment. The reason does not lie in the thing itself which confronts us as an object. It rather lies simply and solely in ourselves, in the

[1] P. Jordan, *Die Physik und das Geheimnis des organischen Lebens* (*Physics and the Secret of Organic Life*), 1941, p. 55.

situation in which we find ourselves when we try to solve the problem of the psychical content of the world by the kind of reasoning which we have described. We who undertake this task are *human* and consequently we are beings to whom only the *human* inner life is directly accessible. Because, entirely without any action on our part, it has fallen to our 'lot' to have entered into existence not as animate molecules or as plants or as individual viruses but as human beings, in our analogical reasoning we can interpret and understand only the language of human vital utterances, human gestures and human words. Because we are human beings, these utterances are for us the form of expression of an inner world which we can deduce from them; while the opening of a rosebud or the growth of a crystal or the humming of a bee is not a form of expression which appeals to us directly. We cannot understand the language of flowers or crystals and we cannot interpret the inner world which perhaps lies hidden behind it, even though we may endeavour with poetic imagination to project our human inner world into these entirely alien beings. It is only because the point of vision of our world-picture, our central vantage point, lies in a human body, that we assume that the sounds which a human body utters and the play of facial expressions which we observe on it are matched by as rich an inner world as we ourselves possess. It is from this fixed point that we start out on our whole line of reasoning, arranging as it were in a series the countless and immensely varied beings with which we are surrounded, from the mammal, which is related to us, down to the plant, and from there to the crystal and to the molecules of which a block of sandstone or a pig of lead is compounded, and placing them in order according to the greater or lesser degree of their similarity to man. When this has been done we assume, in our naïve egocentricity and anthropomorphism, that the inner life of the beings we see around us becomes poorer, less articulate and emptier in exact proportion to their apparent lack of outward resemblance to mankind, until it is no more than a faint presentiment of the wealth of our own vital experience. In our human arrogance we decree that even an animal, a deer which is mortally wounded by a shot or a bull which loses its

G

life in a Spanish bull-ring, shall not 'die' at all but shall simply 'breathe its last'.[1] Dying is the prerogative of us human beings with our rich inner life, and beings which resemble us still less closely than animals do cannot be said even to 'breathe their last'. They simply sink away into nothingness. And just as the experience of death is dependent upon similarity to humanity, so too does the life of the soul in all its other aspects become poorer and meaner the greater the distance that separates it from the sublime exemplar of man. It falls to zero and is extinguished in the night of total unconsciousness when we reach the end of the scale and the nadir of total lack of similarity to mankind, the condition, for example, of the rigid substance of an inorganic being.

This whole gradation which we have set up here, this descending scale of beings, together with all the inferences we draw from it, is, as we have seen, nothing more than the foreshortened view of reality as we see it in perspective from our human standpoint and within our human horizon. Just as, seen from the particular point where I am standing, the birds flying in the air and the stars shining in the night sky appear smaller in proportion to their distance from this point, so too does the inner life of other beings, viewed from my human angle, appear more and more meagre in proportion to their remoteness from mankind. To think we can derive objective knowledge from this foreshortened impression would be just as naïve as was our childhood assumption that the sun, the moon and the stars were really not much larger than they appeared to be when we looked up from our vantage point on the earth and saw them in the sky.

Once we are clear about this, we must seriously endeavour to free ourselves radically from the naïve picture of reality with all its foreshortenings of perspective, a picture to which we have been led by a false presupposition. Just as in the theory of relativity an attempt has been made to reduce the movements of bodies within the universe by the use of transformation equations to a mathematical expression indepen-

---

[1] The German verb is *verenden*, which means *die* and is properly used only of shot game or slaughtered cattle. *Translator*.

dent of the choice of reference body, so here too we must find a completely neutral basis, independent of the countless perspective pictures which are possible in the problem of the psychical content of the world according to whether one looks at it from the standpoint of a human being or from the standpoint of some other being which may possess an overall view which is quite the reverse of the human one. If, for example, my point of vision were in a molecule, then the inner world of this molecule would stand brightly lighted before my eyes, while the gigantic structure of a human body, which from the molecular standpoint would appear as large as a whole solar system appears to us, would only be visible to me from without, and I should perhaps draw the conclusion that the hypothesis that this structure might have a soul and carry within it a hidden inner world was at least as fantastic and questionable as the astronomer Kepler's notion of the animation of the celestial bodies now appears to us.

As soon as we even begin to look for this neutral ground from which the whole problem of the psychical content of nature assumes an entirely different appearance from that which it presented when we looked at it from within our limited human range of vision, we become particularly intensely aware of something which Rainer Maria Rilke expressed so very strikingly in his Duino Elegies. We see ourselves, mankind, as extraordinarily alien beings in the midst of this enigmatic world of which we can view by far the greatest part only objectively from without, while its inner life remains eternally strange and inaccessible to us. Perhaps nothing more profound has ever been said about the inner life of the animal than Rilke's lines in the eighth Duino Elegy:

> With all its eyes the creature sees into the open . . .
> What is out there we know only from the face of the
>   animal;
> For even the early child
> We turn backwards, and compel it to look behind it
> At fashioning and not into the open which is
> So deep in the eyes of the animal. Free from death . . .

We alone see death; the animal is free,
Has its downfall always behind it
And God before it, and, when it goes, it goes
Into eternity as fountains go.
We have never, not one single day,
The one space before us into which the flowers
Are incessantly assumed; it is always the world
And never, nowhere undenied . . .
Who has turned us backwards so that we,
Whatever we may do, are always standing
Like one who is departing? . . .
And who on the last hill, which once more displays
All his valley to him,
Turns, halts, lingers—
That is how we live and endlessly take our departure!

If we allow these lines of Rilke's to work upon us, with their suggestion of the inner superiority of the free animal over our own backward-turned, reflected human existence, they convey to us, far more clearly than any long theoretical considerations could do, the feeling that we have greatly overstepped the proper limits of our judgment if we regard as poorer than ourselves the many creatures around us whose objective forms of expression we do not understand. How can we possibly claim to know that! After all, all we can ever say is that the inner world which lies behind the outward expression (and this is all we can see) is *different* from our own, and is indeed the more so in proportion to our failure to understand its utterances.

The French philosopher Bergson in his *Évolution créatrice* put forward the conjecture that, if we human beings have become craftsmen and achieved such a high degree of technical skill that we think we can master the world by it, this is perhaps only because in one crucial respect we are inwardly very much poorer than all other living things. We are of all beings the most lacking in instinct. Indeed this word instinct, which we are using here, is only a human expression for an inner life which we human beings cannot penetrate or understand because we ourselves lack it. To

2.4695

select only one example from among thousands, let us take the case of the funnel-roller, which makes a curved incision in a birch leaf along a line which runs in such a way that the leaf will roll up and form a small bag well adapted to provide for all the needs of the next generation. The purpose which we human beings achieve in a laborious roundabout way with our mathematical computations and technical considerations —our mathematicians have indeed already studied the funnel-roller's curve—is achieved far more simply and directly and far more surely by this beetle than would ever be possible for us, and it does it by a clairvoyant instinct. If we consider these instinctive actions we are at once faced with the question whether perhaps behind these acts of clairvoyance on the part of animals and plants there may be an inner world which in at least one all-important respect contains far richer possibilities than does all our human craftsmanship and technical activity. If the slow motions of the plants and trees appear to us as symptoms of a comatose condition or of a dreamy soul-life, that is clearly only because, as has already been pointed out, we have considered this vegetable life solely from our human angle and have therefore misunderstood it. Seen under the time-lens the plant moves in at least as lively and as passionate a manner as we do. It is only because we human beings have a different tempo that we have drawn erroneous conclusions from the completely unrelated rhythm of vegetable life. A plant, too, in order to live and to grow, has to fight against thousands of enemies, and this struggle may perhaps be paralleled by as rich a soul-life as our own, but one which extends over longer periods of time. And since atomic physics has resolved the rigidity of lifeless matter into infinitesimal spaces in which elemental particles execute purposeful movements at enormous velocities like living individuals, the last possible reason has been eliminated for regarding the inorganic world as an unconscious inanimate mass. Once again we are simply being naïvely presumptuous if we suppose that because these worlds in which the electrons and protons circle, infinitesimally small as they are according to human standards, have nothing in common in shape or size with a human body, it follows that the inner life too of these unimaginably tiny beings is negligible in comparison with all the joys and sorrows, struggles and defeats, which a human soul experiences.

Here again, if we free ourselves entirely from the human perspective, all that we can say with regard to this world of the small and ultra-small beings is that what takes place with the self-multiplying molecules, for example, is not necessarily merely 'a trace of sentience'. Just because it is unintelligible to us human beings, it is not necessarily any poorer than our own inner experience. It is simply different, totally different from our human inner world. And so we must reckon with the possibility that this whole world of inorganic substances may also be an animate world. Then the saying in the Upanishads would be true: 'Soul alone is this universe.'

In the course of what we have been saying, so far, we have first of all been led up to this thought (which we encounter already in the Indian books of wisdom) by a process of observation and by way of the analogical inferences which force themselves upon us when we look deeply and with open eyes into the richness of the life of nature and of mankind. We are led to the same conclusion from quite a different direction if we set out from the underlying principles which we established in the first chapters of this section with regard to the basic form of our personal existence and of the entire course of cosmic events of which we are members. According to Heidegger, the basic form, in which the deepest essence of our existence lies enclosed, is *time*. And indeed according to the New Testament the form of existence in which we, together with the entire world, are situated is the 'temporal' which is contrasted with the form of existence of 'eternity'. Consideration of this fundamental form of the world consequently leads us from another angle to the problem of universal animation or the psychical nature of the universe (*Allbeseelung*), since already in the chapter on 'the will and events in the world' it became clear to us that we cannot conceive a real passage of time without presupposing the ego which plays a decisive part in bringing this passage of time about. Why is the ego necessary in order to render the passage of time possible? The time series can indeed be conceived without any difficulty as a series of time points, t, t_1, t_2 and so on, following one another in a definite sequence. This series of points may be compared with a strip of film in which the single instantaneous pictures are arranged in order in a definite sequence, no matter whether the film is being passed through the projector or is stored away somewhere in a state of rest. But this sequence of time-points is still not a real passage of time. It is an abstraction in which something is left out of account that is necessarily an essential ingredient of real time. A real passage of time takes place only when, metaphorically speaking, the film strip of the time series is passed through the projector. This means that, of the many instantaneous photographs which succeed one another on the strip of film, at this moment one particular photograph acquires the special significance of being *now*. *Now* is the boundary point which divides the time series into two parts, one of which has already elapsed while the other is still in the lap of the future. The first part of the course of events has already been decided, but for the second part the decision has yet to be made. But the point *now*, which marks this division, cannot be established at all—and this is of crucial importance for our problem—unless an ego is present, applying a demonstrative pronoun to a definite point in time and saying of it: '*This* position within the time series is *my* time, the time in which I am living, the time to which I with my whole existence am linked by my destiny.' I cannot define the words 'today', 'the present' or 'now' without referring to myself in the definition. If I leave myself out of it, then it is quite impossible to express what is meant by these words. If I speak in the present tense, I assume the existence of my own ego.

It is not only as a human being that I stand in the midst of the stream of time which is inconceivable without a point *now*. The whole world is carried away together with me into this irresistible flood. The whole of reality is passing, together with me, through the critical moment which separates the already decided past from the still undecided future. Consequently, if the *now* presupposes an ego which lives through it, then it is not merely behind every human life that there lies an ego, forming its invisible substratum, but the whole of world events, the struggle for existence of the beasts, the growth of plants, the circling of the planets around the sun and of the electrons around the nucleus, all must be related to something which presents some analogy, however distant, with what in the human sphere we call an ego. We know nothing of the way in which the 'ego beings' (*Ichwesen*), of which we must here assume the existence, are distributed in the various organic and inorganic regions of reality as a whole. If we attempt to make any *positive* assertions about them on the basis of analogical inferences, we are groping in the dark. But the one *negative* statement which alone concerns us in the present context, a statement which we must apply equally to all these beings, is clear and unambiguous: they all stand outside the space of objectivity.

We can form a clear picture of this negative fact if we con-sider the position occupied within the time series by the point *now*, from which the ego looks out in both directions, back-wards into the past and forwards into the future. If we begin by looking out backwards from the point *now* into the past, occurrences which still belong to the immediate present, i.e. which still stand in the zenith of *now*, are quite clearly distinguishable from what is already over, in that they have not yet become objective (cf. *Glaube und Denken* (*Belief and Thought*), 4, p. 17. The unity of the two relations—ego and object and becoming and having become, p. 110ff.). Martin Buber says in his book *I and Thou* that 'objects consist in having been'. In other words, whatever confronts me as an object is no longer the immediate present. In order to become objective, an event must be separated from the point *now* by an interval of time, however short. It must already belong to the past. If, for example, something is to be audible to me as the sound of a violin, then the point of time when the sound wave left the vibrating string and throbbed through the air must precede by at least a fraction of a second the point *now* at which it confronts me objectively. If a visible object is to appear before my eyes, a constellation in the night sky, perhaps, or the flash of a pocket lamp, then the ray which produces this picture must have been emitted already before the moment *now*. For our present problem it is of no great importance whether the point of origin of the ray precedes the point *now* by a period of decades, as is the case with certain stars, or whether the time differential is extremely small, as it is in the case of the pocket lamp which flashes close before my eyes. What matters is that if anything is to confront me as an objective picture, then its objectivisation must already have taken place. In other words, it must already have crossed the boundary which separates the present from the past. And so, strictly speaking, whatever I am able to see as an object no longer belongs to the present but is something which 'has been'. Thus any objective experience is in fact a looking back from the point *now* at something past, something which has just *been*. From this it follows that what is itself present, the content of the moment *now,* is still on this side of all objectivity. It has not yet become objective; it has not yet assumed any kind of objective form. Since I myself, with my whole existence, am situated in this *now,* it follows, as H. Rickert says, that my ego is 'non-objectivisable'. For I could confront myself as an object only if an interval of time lay between myself and the consciousness which I have of my existence. Only then could I precede my consciousness in time and so become an object of my consciousness as something which 'has been'. But as it is, my consciousness of myself coincides with me myself in a single point of time. Consequently my consciousness of myself cannot confront me myself as an object.

Yet it is not only when I look out backwards into the past from the point *now* that I distinguish myself from the whole objective world as something non-objective, but also when I look forwards into the future. For, as we saw in the chapter entitled 'The Will and Events in the World', the will as such is quite distinct from the deed in which it achieves realization and is precipitated on the objective plane as well as from all the conceptions, plans and thoughts with which this realization is prepared within my consciousness. The will itself stands on the threshold between past and future, as a non-objective reality on this side of all these forms in which it finds its objective expression, when, from the present state of becoming, the new world-configuration of the future is born. Thus, whether we look backwards into the past or forwards into the future, we perceive the astonishing fact that the boundary point, through which time is continually passing in its incessant march out of the concluded past into the still undecided future, belongs to a space which is totally different from that of the objective time series. In an earlier chapter we compared the point *now* with a winding-drum held as though by an invisible power always at the same place while time is wound on to it like a rope and is then reeled off it again. The *now* does not participate in the movement of the time series. As the *nunc aeternum,* the eternal now, it is not borne away by the stream of time. From one point of view, certainly, it is one point amid an infinity of other points which succeed one another within the time series. But from the other point of view it lies outside the whole passage of time; it has no location whatever within the objective space of time but belongs to the non-objective space. It is the position at which the non-objectivisable ego is mysteriously linked with the time series.

In all this we have been attempting to describe the way in which events take place in time, passing from the obscure future into the present, the molten state of becoming, and then solidifying as the unalterable past. But this movement of time is not merely a *human* experience. It is the law to which the whole course of cosmic happenings is subject. It is therefore together with the whole of reality that we human beings advance at every successive instant through the *nunc aeternum,* in which an encounter takes place between this objective world and a space which lies outside objectivity, a space of which the content is not objectivisable. The whole of world events passes together with us through this obscure space in which everything is invisible, unobservable and shrouded in night. Under cover of this darkness the new cosmic instant is born. This is where the hidden sources well up from which all decisions proceed—not only the volitional resolutions through which we human beings intervene from a higher dimension in the course of the objective processes of nature, directing it according to our plans by means of our technical skill, but also the clairvoyant instinct of animals and plants and the incalculable movements of the electrons, which we can only register statistically. Everything, together with us, in the darkness of the non-objectivisable space passes through the great transformation in which the current of temporal events is converted from the fluid state of undecided possibilities, still resting in the womb of the future, into the solid condition of the past, where occurrences have become history and have thus acquired a definite shape which remains unalterable for evermore in the clear bright light of objective space.

We cross the boundary between past and future in company with many other beings which stand invisible behind the whole of non-human nature, and consequently the *now*, which constitutes this boundary, is not merely a boundary *point* but a boundary line that is passed over by infinitely many beings at once. The beings in whose company we cross this border are, during this fateful moment, not merely themselves just as non-objectivisable as we are, but even the manner of our being together with them at this point of time belongs to the non-objective space. We cannot regard them objectively. We cannot see into them. They are 'our unknown brothers', as Julie Schlosser calls the animals. As has been seen, we can establish indirect communication with them in a roundabout way through the medium of the objective world and draw conclusions inferential regarding their inner nature. And yet we know about their existence in just the same mysterious and non-objectivisable way as we know about our own. For indeed each of us knows about himself, even though he is not able to look into himself as he might look into a room or some other objective space. Each one of us is conscious of being a cognitive subject, looking out backwards from the point *now* into the past, and a volitional subject, looking out forwards from the point *now* and fighting, in conflict and in alliance with other ego-beings, to decide the shape of the future. We cannot therefore help suspecting that our fellow beings too, which stand side by side with us in the same field of battle, possess some kind of knowledge of themselves, more or less analogous with our own self-awareness.

From all this we have seen that we are led to the idea that everything is animate (*der Gedanke der Allbeseelung*) not only when we follow the path of observation and analogical inference, as we first did, but also when we approach the problem from a quite different direction with a fundamental consideration of the nature of the point *now* and of the archetypal form of temporality which determines the configuration of all occurrences in time.

9. THE DECISIVE TURNING-POINT IN THE HISTORY OF HUMAN THOUGHT

In the last chapter two different approaches compelled us to accept at least the possibility that the entire world is animate. This leads us on to the idea that the objective world, with which in the natural sciences we are exclusively concerned, the world which we can illuminate and investigate experimentally with the microscope and the telescope, is not the whole of reality but is only *one* space into which everything is fitted. There exists simultaneously a second space which, together with the whole of reality, we traverse at every instant and which surrounds us from all sides just as the space of objectivity does. This is the non-objective space in which the I and the Thou encounter one another. We must begin by looking back briefly at the course of the history of ideas in the past, in order to make clear how the discovery of this second space was prepared and how, in the course of the last century, this discovery has brought about a change in our thinking which even today has still not reached completion.

Primitive man, and every modern child, too, until it is well over ten years old, lives as a matter of course and without reflecting upon it in *one* space only, the perceptual space of his visible bodily environment which surrounds him with all the power of what can be grasped and seen and in which everything that confronts him—houses, trees, mountains and human beings—has its place. Anyone who lives only in one space does not in truth live in any space at all. The concept of space has not yet occurred to him and he has given no thought to it. The thinking of primitive man is consequently much simpler, clearer and more coherent than the thinking of the civilized man of a later age, in whose world-picture a confusing rôle is played by such invisible realities as 'soul' and 'spirit' which he cannot conceive as anything observable. For primitive man there is no reality which is not observable and corporeal. If a fellow tribesman who has died appears to him in a dream, he concludes from this that a man possesses a kind of shadowy double who is now already living in his body and who will leave it at his death. This double may either set out to wander through the land of shades or else visit the living at night. For this reason primitive man buries together with the dead man's body weapons and food for his travels. In a number of African tribes the dead man is placed in a boat together with all that is needed for a voyage. The boat is launched on to a river, upon which the dead man is supposed to float away to the land of shades. If the primitive man, living only in the one space of the corporeal, observable world, believes in divine beings, then these must in his conception be corporeal, observable beings. The 'world beyond', in which they dwell and from which they may occasionally come down to earth, cannot be anything other than a part of the one space which exists, in other words an upper storey of our own cosmos. The divine beings are 'up in heaven', while mankind is 'here below on earth'. Later on, at the time of the Ptolemaic conception of the structure of the universe, this means that the divine beings dwell above the empyrean, the fiery heaven, that is to say in the region which lies beyond the sphere of Saturn, the most distant of the planets then known. In Christian terms, it is up above the empyrean that God sits enthroned. It is from up there that Christ came down to earth to us; thither he returned at his Ascension and from thence he shall come again with the clouds of Heaven. That is the first primitive stage of human thinking, the stage at which there is only one space.

The second phase begins at the moment when, like an irruption from the subconscious into the conscious mind, there comes the first faint notion that this whole existence within the observable world may perhaps not be the only form of existence and that there may perhaps be some other mode of being which differs fundamentally from this observable existence not only in its content but in its entire configuration. This notion cannot have entered men's minds through philosophical reflection. A man whose entire thinking is conducted in terms of *one* space cannot possibly be persuaded by logical argument that some other space may exist. For a space always appears to us at first as a self-contained world, comprising everything which forms part of reality, and consequently immune against any attempt to break in from outside with philosophical arguments. The great reorientation which led to the awakening in us of the notion that some other existence is possible must have arisen not from theoretical reflection but from a cataclysmic shock, disturbing the vital centre of man and thus shaking the foundations and the walls of the immense prison in which he is confined. It is only later that this shock suffered by the whole existence of man produces its effect in his thinking as well. In the history of the Indian people this mysterious change took place when the strong and warlike tribes had come down from the north into the torrid valleys of India and, perhaps as a consequence of a certain weakening of their original vitality, were overcome with an enigmatic nostalgic longing to leave the whole world of multiplicity and return to the All-One. It was only later that this sudden change in their whole emotional attitude to life crystallized in a philosophical form in the final part of the Vedas, the Upanishads, with the transformation of the sacrificial ritual of the primitive national religion into a symbol of the merging of the individual ego in the universal ego. A similar and equally enigmatic transformation of their entire underlying attitude to life must have been taking place with the Greeks when Plato wrote his dialogues. Here again, the philosophical system was merely the conceptual product of an existential change which had already transformed the entire personality.

This is evident from the fact that the philosophical expression of the change which supervened did not keep pace with the change itself but at first lagged behind it. Plato's thought is a transitional phase which still betrays some characteristics of the primitive thought out of which it developed. Plato was indeed aware of the great gulf that separates our ego, of which we are conscious when we withdraw into ourselves, from the physical world which confronts us objectively. But when he tried to express this opposition in philosophical terms, the only distinction he was able to draw was that between the transitory individual things in the sensible world and the permanent essence (οὐσία) in which the 'idea' combines the common properties of things so as to form a higher unity (e.g. the idea of the sphere in relation to the many individual spheres of which the spherical shape is the common property). The ego, the 'soul', in Plato's opinion belongs together with this permanent essence. In thus grouping the soul together with the οὐσία, Platonism obviously does not really advance beyond the spatial conception of the primitives. For the οὐσία is still nothing more than a combination of the common properties of similar things in the observable objective world. Consequently, Plato's 'soul' is strictly speaking merely a substance which differs from other substances in that it is indivisible; it is an indivisible, and therefore, so Plato concludes, an indestructible thing. But things in space may not only be distinguished from one another abstractly; they may also be separated from one another concretely, i.e. taken apart and put together again. That is why, according to Plato, there is nothing to prevent the soul from separating itself from the body and continuing to exist in a disembodied state. While the body disintegrates or is reduced to ashes, the soul may leave it as a prisoner leaves his cell or as a bird soars freely into the air when its cage is opened. Hence there arose the Platonic belief in immortality, which as soon as it was enunciated exercised a power of immense seduction over men's minds, because it freed them from the fear of death and satisfied their hunger for life. The idea of immortality, which persisted not only in the great medieval systems, which were still under the direct influence of Plato, but even in rationalism and the enlightenment, could arise only because Plato, in formulating philosophically the opposition of which he had become aware between the ego and the objective world, was still thinking in terms of the primitive conception of space. It is no mere coincidence that it was precisely Plato who, together with Aristotle, called a halt to the tendency to reject the geocentric cosmology, although the geocentric conception had already a hundred years earlier been seriously challenged by the triumphant advance of the Greek mind. It was because of them that this geocentric view retained its hold on men's minds for the ensuing two thousand years. The Ptolemaic conception of the universe as a space divided into an upper and a lower storey, and the Platonic division of man into a mortal and an immortal component, both are offshoots of one and the same development. Both derive from the primitive conception of space, from which Plato, despite his new breadth of vision, was still unable to free himself. The tenaciously defended stronghold of the objective space conception of the primitives could not be overcome at the first assault. It was first necessary to pass through a transitional phase. The residue of primitive thinking, which had persisted even into the age of rationalism, was still not really eliminated even in the next stage, that of Fichte's *Theory of Science*, although Fichte had made a discovery which led far beyond Plato. For Fichte the ego was not a substance— neither a divisible one nor an indivisible one. It was rather, in opposition to the entire objective universe, the non-objective subject, separated from the whole of objectivity by a deep gulf. This was the great step forward by which German idealism surpassed Plato. This point of departure in Fichte's thought was an achievement comparable with that of Copernicus. This was the first discovery of the non-objectivisable ego in its fundamental opposition to the beginning and ending of human bodies and solar systems. In the 'atheism controversy', which Fichte fought out to the end against a stick-in-the-mud body of theologians around the turn of the century, the theological consequences of the new discovery were drawn and the struggle against the 'objective god' was carried through to a victorious conclusion. After that this new discovery could no longer be lost sight of.

But even this new view was still marred by one last trace of the primitive conception of space. Even Fichte still believed that the non-objective ego could be detached and raised above the objective world with which it was for the time being connected, just as an aeroplane, after standing on the ground, leaves the ground behind it and soars into the air when the engine is started, without any change taking place either in the aeroplane or in the ground it has left. That is how the seductive thought arose which was so stirringly expressed in those phrases of Fichte's which have already been quoted: 'Even though my body may decay and become dust, even though the whole world may vanish away, yet when the last sun has sent forth its last spark of light, I shall soar bravely and coldly above all that, and I shall remain the same I that I am today.' In reading these bold sentences one is involuntarily reminded of an air-balloon hovering calmly in the air above a raging torrent. Sitting in this balloon I can enjoy the spectacle of the whole transitory world being swept away by the wild river of time, all the catastrophes of human history and all the cataclysms which mark the ends of worlds.

Kant, that incorruptible guardian of the frontiers of German thought, already saw clearly that this seductive notion, which over and over again intoxicated men's minds all the way from Plato to Fichte, was simply an unresolved residue of primitive thinking, which regarded the ego too as a thing, capable of being detached and removed from other things. Kant demonstrated that the cognitive ego, the subject of knowing, cannot be the object of objective knowledge. Consequently it cannot be separated from other things by a 'concrete detachment' but always only distinguished from the world of experience by means of an abstraction. By recognizing this fact, Kant subjected the quasi-Copernican discovery which had been achieved by German idealism to a critical examination and cleansed it of the impurities which it had retained from the primitive conception of space. Only one last step still remained to be taken in order to leave behind this transitional phase through which, from Plato to Kant, human thought was still passing, and to reach the final stage at which we find ourselves today. Indeed Kant himself prepared the way for this last stage of development, but he did not set foot in the new territory which is thus opened up. He

H

is like Moses, who from the summit of Mount Nebo saw the promised land spread out in the sunshine but was himself not permitted to enter it. Together with Fichte he had recognized that on this side of the whole observable space there lies a region which is not observable; and he had seen that between this observable world and that non-observable region in which I stand as the cognitive ego there is a great gulf fixed. But at the same time he also saw that the two worlds, extremely different as they are, nevertheless belong together so intimately that they cannot be separated by any 'concrete detachment' but can only be distinguished from one another by means of an abstraction. Only one step now remains to be taken in order to reach the final recognition which brings to an end the whole process which began with primitive thought. The reason must still be made clear why only an abstract distinction between the two worlds is possible. It is because the opposition here is not between two *worlds* but between two *spaces,* the relation between which can therefore not be compared with any intra-spatial relation. This can only be completely understood when the new mathematics and the new physics have begun to reckon with a multiplicity of spaces, and when, simultaneously, in the age of existential philosophy, thinkers have also begun to devote attention to the Thou.

10. THE GRAIN OF TRUTH IN THE DOCTRINE OF METEMPSYCHOSIS AND REINCARNATION

Before proceeding to an examination of the conception of space formulated by contemporary mathematics and physics, we must first draw two clear distinctions in order to define the result to which this decisive turn in the history of human thought has led. First of all we must distinguish between the discovery of the non-objective space and the transitional phase which we find still in the case of Plato and even in the case of Fichte, both of whom indeed already based their thinking on the new discovery, yet still expressed it in the form of primitive thought. And on the other hand, it must be kept clearly in mind that, although I can distinguish myself as a non-objectivisable reality from the whole objective world, it is nevertheless impossible to separate me from objectivity by a 'concrete detachment'. It is just as it was with the distinction between the uni-dimensional time-space and the three-dimensional body-space. These two spaces, in which we always simultaneously stand, can of course at any moment be clearly distinguished in the abstract, but it is quite impossible to separate three-dimensional space from the time-series. Every body always participates in the irresistible movement of the passage of time. Thus in our human existence too we stand in two quite different spaces, and yet this existence is an indissoluble union between the non-objectivisable ego and the destiny which links it to a definite position within the plane of objectivity. Consequently my ego is not a 'psychical substance' such as might be detached and removed from my body like a prisoner leaving his cell or a bird its cage, so that I might then live on, freed from all the fetters of the objective world, in a disembodied existence. If that is impossible, it follows that all the metaphysical consequences which can be drawn from the conception of a disembodied existence of the psychical substance must from the outset be abandoned. The concrete ego must always be linked with some variable element belonging to the objective form of the physical world. Otherwise we relapse again into the Platonic transitional phase.

We must draw an equally definite distinction between the result we have now achieved and the world-picture of the primitives who have still not accomplished the reorientation which it has been our concern to describe. This second distinction is nowadays perhaps more necessary than the first, for in many circles at present people are inclined to disassociate themselves as completely as they can from the 'Greek understanding of man', even at the risk of falling back into the view of man which was held by the primitives. In the primitive view, man as an animate body is, of course, a piece of objective space, the only space which primitive man recognizes. In contrast to this view, it must be kept clearly in mind that, despite the unity of our personal existence, we are nevertheless always 'wanderers between two worlds', beings which live always simultaneously in two contrasting spaces.

In the *here* and the *now* there is at every instant a new
encounter between two spaces which are related to one another. This is clear to me from the fact that I can indeed see
my body and the whole environment in which it occupies a
definite situation, and yet I cannot see myself. My centre of
vision, before which the whole panorama of world events
unfolds in perspective, is itself invisible and incapable of
objectivisation. It lies outside the whole objective world-
picture and appertains to a space which is distinct from
objectivity. The stream of time, to which the point *now*
belongs, does indeed surge incessantly past me, together with
all the exciting events that succeed one another within it; but
I myself am not a point within the time series. I stand outside it and am always merely linked, at every instant afresh,
with one definite instant within this time series, the instant
which has the special significance of being *now*. It is my
inescapable destiny to live in this instant that is for me the
present in which the die is being cast to decide my future;
and yet I draw a clear distinction between myself and my
destiny. Otherwise I could experience no sorrow at having
been destined to be born just at this difficult time. I know
perfectly well that the tide of fate might in the nature of
things just as well have cast me up at any other point on the
shore of world events, and at a point where it would have
been easier to come to grips with life. It must therefore be
asserted quite explicitly that even though it is my *fate* to be
tied to this *here* and *now* and this human individual, even
though it is my *destiny* to be a human being at all and not
some other being, yet I am not myself identical with this
destiny. I distinguish myself from my destiny just as clearly
as an actor distinguishes himself from the rôle which he has
to play for the duration of an evening. I myself am not this
human body. I am not this human being. I am not a human
being at all.

This clear distinction between my self and the destiny
which, through no action of my own, was allotted to me when
I entered into this existence, my destiny to play the rôle of a
human being and of this particular human being—this clear
distinction is not merely of theoretical significance; it is also

of decisive practical importance for the whole of our human life in common. The understanding and forgiving love, which we must bring to bear in our dealings with a fellow human being with whom we have to live and work together every day, rests ultimately upon my making a clear distinction between his ego and the destiny which has fallen to his lot and which perhaps occasions him the most suffering of all, the destiny to be precisely that human individual and to bear the burden of that existence until it is taken from him by death. It is only when I cease to identify my companion with his destiny, but distinguish clearly between him himself and the fate which makes him this individual, that I begin to understand from within and to share the burden of everything about him which repels or irritates me and so to fulfil the command 'Bear ye one another's burdens'. This distinction of great theoretical and practical importance between the ego and its destiny to be this particular human being is expressed mythologically in the doctrine of metempsychosis and reincarnation, which is nowadays springing up again in every possible form. Belief in reincarnation comes down to us, as Lessing emphasizes, from the very earliest human philosophies of life. It is predominant especially in Indian thought, particularly in Buddhism, and it is fairly certainly from there that it came to Greece. Lessing and Goethe both accepted it. If Christianity rejects it, that is not because we find it inconceivable in itself, but solely because, as Thielicke[1] quite rightly emphasizes, by introducing into human life the 'repeatability' of natural processes this belief violates the principle that 'human life and death can only happen once'. This deprives our life of the extreme earnestness and responsibility which are implied in its non-repeatability. Yet even though this ethical consideration compels us to reject the idea of reincarnation, that should not make us lose sight of the grain of truth in it which is demonstrated by the fact that this idea keeps springing up again in new forms in the history of human thought, despite all the objections that have been raised against it. The grain of truth in this primeval belief lies in

[1] Helmut Thielicke, *Tod und Leben* (*Death and Life*), J. C. B. Mohr, Tübingen, 1945, p. 6off.

the distinction which it makes between the constant ego, which always retains its identity, and the destiny which has fallen to its lot, to be attached for the duration of life to a particular human being.   Undoubtedly the most impressive mythological formulation of this idea is the myth, deriving from the Pythagorean tradition, which forms the conclusion of Plato's *Republic*.   The souls, which have been journeying through the world, are brought in the Beyond before a messenger of Lachesis.   He stands on a high platform and addresses them as follows: ' Thus saith unto you the daughter of Necessity, the maiden Lachesis.   Ephemeral souls!   This is the beginning of another death-bringing circuit for your mortal race.   Your destiny is not determined by the dæmon. It is you who choose the dæmon for yourselves.   But when once one of you has drawn his lot, he has thereby chosen the course upon which he must irrevocably remain.'   And then the 'lots' and 'life patterns' are displayed before the souls for them to make their choice.   One soul chooses a swan, another a nightingale, a third a lion.   The soul of Agamemnon, hating the human race because of the hurts he has suffered, chooses the life of an eagle in exchange.   The joker Thersites wants to turn into a monkey.   But the soul of Odysseus, healed of all ambition by the memory of the sufferings he has endured, looks this way and that and at last finds the destiny of a peaceable citizen, standing entirely aloof from all affairs of state.   This myth demonstrates plainly that one must distinguish clearly the 'soul' itself from the 'lot' and the 'pattern of life' that are assigned to it by a decision which takes place already before it is born and which it no longer remembers.   It is tied to this allotted destiny for its whole present existence 'irrevocably'.

We have now circumscribed the conclusion to which this chapter has led us, distinguishing it sharply both from the transitional phase of Platonic thought and from the purely objective thinking of the primitives.   We must climb along a narrow ridge between two precipices, in continual danger of falling into one or the other.   Only thus can we properly approach all the problems which arise from what we have learnt so far.   The attitude which enables us to avoid both these perils will become clearest to us if we end by looking once more at the New Testament. In the present context we may still leave out of account the most profound meaning of this book, for it is only in a later chapter that we intend to approach the problem of God. But the New Testament, this profoundly significant document which has come down to us from the later period of classical antiquity, reveals to us particularly clearly the narrow path that leads us through between the two abysses which, in view of what has been said, we must at all costs avoid.

If we ask whether the men who speak to us in the New Testament still belong to the primitive phase or whether they are able to conceive the idea of reincarnation, there can be no doubt about the answer. The apostles, and especially Paul, who speaks most clearly about this problem, quite consciously repudiated the late Jewish belief regarding the future, the belief in which they had been brought up but which was still based on primitive conceptions. The Jew of that period wanted to be laid in his grave with a particular coat and with a staff in his hand; for he supposed that he would rise again just as he had been at the time of his burial and would go in that guise to meet the Messiah. Only when he had re-emerged from the earth, still in the same form, would the judgment take place which must decide whether this body was to be destroyed for ever or whether it was to enter glorified into the Messianic kingdom. Thus the late Jewish belief in resurrection was based on the primitive notion according to which man was an animate body which must either be entirely destroyed or else entirely restored. Paul thought quite differently. According to the assertions contained in the chapter on resurrection (I Cor. 15.35ff. and II Cor. 5.1ff.), death signifies the final annihilation of our present body which is made of earth. The earthly 'tabernacle' in which we now dwell collapses. The frail tent is struck. The tattered earthly garment falls from us. And if there is to be any further existence for us at all, 'if so be that we shall not be found naked', which appears to the apostle as an impossible condition, then this can be achieved in only one way, namely through a 're-embodiment'. My ego, after the first taber-

nacle has collapsed, must have a completely new abode bestowed upon it, an abode which has nothing to do with the
old, fragile tabernacle, a house which is a 'building of God'
and which already stands prepared for us in the heavens, so
that we even now 'have' it (II Cor. 5.1). Or, to employ the
other metaphor, when the old, tattered garment has fallen
from us, a new garment is lying prepared for us, a garment
with which Paul hopes to be covered and 'clothed upon' at
once, so that at the change from the old body to the new there
can be no interval of bodilessness.

If, then, we wish to assign the New Testament to its proper
place in the line of development which leads from the primitive phase of human thought to the present day, we must say
that it is already beyond the initial stage of human thinking,
in which the person is regarded as nothing more than an
animate organism occupying a particular situation in physical
space. For the New Testament, just as for Plato and his
successors, the ego is rather something other than this human
body, and this makes possible what would have been inconceivable for primitive man, namely the reincarnation of the
ego in a new body. Up to this point the New Testament
agrees with Plato, but here they part company. The diver-
gence between the apostles' thought and Plato's human
understanding is to be found at two points. Firstly, according
to the Indian and Platonic belief in metempsychosis, the ego
can change its abode as often as it likes and settle repeatedly
in new bodies; whereas in the New Testament this change
can take place only once, namely at the dawn of a new aeon,
which began with the resurrection of Christ but will achieve
its consummation only at the end of the world. And secondly,
the apostles do not stop short at the transitional phase which
we find in Plato and Fichte, the stage at which the primitive
conception of space still makes itself felt; they do not believe
that the ego can be simply separated from the physical world
by means of a 'concrete detachment' and continue to exist
in a disembodied state. The ego is not, indeed, bound once
and for all to one particular corporeality, but some corporeality or other is necessary if it is really to exist. According to Paul it is an intolerable condition for the ego if it is

found 'naked', that is to say without a bodily covering. In recognizing this fact, Paul stands close to the threshold of the final phase, the phase in which we are at last freed from the limitations of the primitive conception of space; but, of course, as an apostle, he had no reason to seek for a philosophical formulation of the fact which he had discerned. This is the discovery towards which Kant's work points the way, the discovery that the ego on the one hand and our body on the other are not only two different forms of existence but that they belong to two different spaces, spaces which possess fundamentally different structures but are nevertheless so intimately united that they can be distinguished only by means of an abstraction.

This clear distinction between two spaces in which we live simultaneously is again drawn in the words which Christ addresses to his disciples when He sends them out to face deadly peril: 'Fear not them which kill the body, but are not able to kill the soul' (Matt. 10.28). The $\sigma\hat{\omega}\mu\alpha$, the body, which belongs to the objective world, lies exposed to the forces of annihilation which match their strength together in mortal conflict on the objective plane. But the soul, the $\psi\nu\chi\acute{\eta}$, stands apart from this whole battlefield. It is immune against all the destructive weapons of this earth, 'shell-proof' against all earthly missiles. Its destiny is subject to another law than that which governs all processes within the objective world. The $\psi\nu\chi\acute{\eta}$, advancing invulnerable through all earthly battles, is nothing other than the *ego,* which is linked with the physical world and which nevertheless stands outside this world. For Christ's famous saying about the soul, and how it is more important to preserve it than to conquer the whole world, is rendered in St. Luke's Gospel as follows: 'For what is a man advantaged, if he gain the whole world, and lose himself ($\dot{\epsilon}\alpha\nu\tau\acute{o}\nu$), or be cast away?' (Luke 9.25).

Let us now look back once again in order to summarize the conclusion which we have reached in these last chapters. Let us consider the overall picture of reality which results from everything that has so far been said. The ultimate units, which alone are given us immediately and to which alone we have direct access, are, as we saw already in the first chapter, the ego-beings (*Ichwesen*), the 'souls', as they are called by Plato and, in a more profound sense, by the Bible. Each one of us is alone immediately cognisant of himself and is immediately cognisant only of himself. This fundamental fact was taken as the starting-point by Descartes in his *Méditations* and by Fichte in his *Theory of Science*. One's own ego, as Eddington said, is the only place at which each one of us sees directly into the interior of the world. Anything else confronts us only as an object, and therefore at a distance. It is only indirectly accessible to us. With scientific methods we can always only imperfectly penetrate into the hidden objective world. Our chapter on the psychical content of the world has led us to suspect that the existence of these solitary subjects, each alone immediately cognisant of itself and immediately cognisant only of itself, is not confined to our human sphere, but that other non-objective beings, more or less analogous to what we in the human sphere call a soul, are concealed behind non-human nature too, even behind a worm suffering in solitude when it is crushed, even behind a flower frozen to death on a frosty night, perhaps even behind a molecule whose elemental particules execute incalculable movements reminiscent of the decisions of a will. If this conjecture is correct, then these non-objectivisable beings are the irreducible units of which reality is constituted. But the spatial-temporal objective world with which natural science concerns itself has a fundamental significance for the existence of these psychical beings. It is, as we have seen, the medium which alone enables these beings to enter into relations with one another, to come to terms with one another, to affect one another, and to struggle with one another. For each ego-being is entirely alone; it cannot communicate *directly* with another. It can do so only by *indirect* means, namely by virtue of the fact that between the I and the Thou the objective world is placed, like an opaque but impressionable waxen party-wall between two solitary prisoners.

This gives us a picture of reality as a whole consisting of a non-objective region and an objective region. The ego-beings, these irreducible units to which alone we have immediate access and upon which the world rests, are, regarded in isolation, non-objective. They stand, therefore, outside of the entire objective space. They are still not linked by destiny to any point in the time series or to any location in physical space. And so they have still no *now* and no *here*. They still stand outside all the spatial and temporal dimensions which apply within the objective space. This is of crucial importance, for it is only when we ourselves, in our innermost being, are removed from the entire objective space with all its spatial-temporal dimensions, that the philosophical and religious propositions which we assert about ourselves and about the cosmos can have any bearing at all upon the picture of reality as a whole. For if each of us is himself no more than a particle of the spatio-temporal world, occupying a definite place within it, then all our philosophical and theological systems, all the doctrinal conflicts in which we engage together, all the churches we establish, have no relevance whatever to the all-embracing reality, since they all take place within the interior of beings which occupy such an infinitesimally small fraction of the immense cosmic space and of the boundless cosmic time that they are altogether negligible in relation to the whole. They are insignificant, just as a few grains of sand, flying up into the air in a severe sandstorm which whips up the sandhills of the Sahara Desert, would be insignificant in relation to the boundless sandy waste. But in fact as ego-beings we stand, in the depths of our being, in the non-objective space. It is, of course, as we saw at the end of the fourth chapter, only by means of an abstraction that we can disregard the 'variable factor' of our existence, the fact of our being linked to a definite here and now, and that we can become conscious of ourselves as we are, independently of the particular situation within the world of experience to which we stand in a predestined relation. But as soon as I think about myself in this way, I become aware of the extraordinarily important fact that the 'invariable' nucleus of my ego would remain the same even if I could exchange for another position the position to which I am attached within the cosmic space. What I must predicate of myself applies also to every other ego with which I can enter into the I-Thou relation, i.e. not merely to the human subjects which resemble me, but also, *mutatis mutan-dis*, to other psychical beings completely unknown to me, which are present, though invisible, in an immense multitude at every point throughout the entire world of nature. All these beings, of which only a very small proportion are at all exactly known to us, are united, together with us, in the non-objective space. Consequently, they stand, together with us, on this side of all objective dimensions, on this side of the contrast between a spatial length of a millimetre and a length of millions of light-years, and on this side of the difference between a duration of a second and a duration of thousands of millions of years. It is only because they stand outside the entire objective space, the space which can be scientifi-cally surveyed, that the immediate knowledge which these beings have of themselves is of any significance whatever in relation to the immensity of the cosmos which is today dis-closed to us.

The structure of the non-objective space, in which we ego-beings (*Ichwesen*) co-exist together, is such as to give rise to that underlying conflict which, once it is projected on to the plane of objectivity, transforms the whole world into a battlefield. This conflict follows from the mutually exclusive claims of the I and the Thou. Either I, Subject A, am the central pivot of the world, or else you, Subject B, are that centre. This either-or, this all-or-nothing opposition between the I and the Thou, arises already independently of the relationship into which each one of us is destined to enter with some particular position within the world of experience. Even if I could exchange 'my there', the there into which I 'am cast', my here and now, for yours, I could still never exchange my self for your self. Even after this exchange I should still have to remain I and you would still have to remain you. From this we see that the mutually exclusive claim of the I and the Thou, which is the deepest root of all the conflicts that convulse the world, arises already from the structure of the non-objective space, which is still on this side of all the dimensional relations of the objective world. But this non-objective space, as we have seen, cannot exist in isolation. As Kant, unlike Plato and Fichte, clearly recognized, we can only distinguish it from the objective space by means of an abstraction; we cannot detach it from it concretely. It is indeed conceivable that the 'invariable' factor of my personal existence should be detached from this particular position within the world of experience to which it is moored for the duration of life, or in which, as we may also say, it is 'incarnate'. But it cannot, as Plato supposed, soar freely in the air without any incarnation at all. It must be attached to *some* variable factor or other. In this way the objective space acquires its necessary position within the framework of reality as a whole. It is the indispensable medium, the opaque 'party-wall' through which the non-objective ego-beings enter into all the possible kinds of communication with one another. Because of the mutually exclusive pretensions of these beings, the objective space in which their relations with each other are expressed becomes the arena where the deep-seated conflicts between the ego-beings are fought out. And thus the fundamental antagonism, potentially present in the non-objective space, is projected on to the objective plane, where the tension is released in a terrible explosion. If we visualize this general conception of reality, reality appears to us as an immensely wide plain over which there lowers a dark, ominous storm-cloud. From this storm-cloud, which is charged with electricity, lightning flashes down incessantly. The countless beings which inhabit the plain wander across the broad expanse like fugitives, each by itself, homeless and restless, continually threatened by the lightning flashes, to which they are exposed at every step they take.

This general conception of reality, to which the preceding chapters have led us, implies an unresolved dissonance, of which anyone who considers it is at once aware. Since this dissonance arises not merely from the content of the world but from the structure of the spaces of which the whole cosmos is composed, the disharmony cannot really be resolved by any changing of the content. The cosmic disharmony can be resolved only if a new space is disclosed, a space in which the *either-or*, which is the dominant feature of this entire conception, is overcome.

11. THE PROBLEM OF SPACE IN MODERN PHYSICS

In the next section we shall discuss the settlement of the conflict implied in the general conception of reality which all our considerations so far have led us to accept; but first of all the concept of space, which is of crucial importance for the solution of the cosmic enigma, must be clarified, at least so far as is necessary in order to render this settlement intelligible. The rift between belief and natural science can today be bridged, and mutual comprehension established, only if it is possible to transpose the concept of space, which has acquired a position of primary significance in modern physics, in a higher connotation to the world-picture of belief. The question of whether and by what means this is possible can be decided only if we first consider for a moment the far-reaching transformation of the concept of space which is taking place in contemporary physics. The question of the nature of space has, during the past eighty years or so, been reopened for discussion in mathematics and physics from entirely new points of view. In the present context we can deal only with the central problem with which this reconsideration of the nature of space is concerned, a problem upon which opinion is still divided.

If the close connexion which still prevailed in Kant's time between philosophy and the natural sciences has today become a very loose one, and if a certain tension has developed between these two branches of research, the main reason for this lies in the fact that the conception of space which has been more and more generally accepted in physics since Helmholtz, and especially since Einstein and the advent of quantum mechanics, and which has led to some astonishing discoveries, has come into conflict with the theory of space which forms part of the foundations of the Kantian system and which is widely maintained, even today, by the neo-Kantians.[1] According to Kant, the intuitional forms of space and time are not contained in the 'thing in itself', but are 'merely a subjective

[1] The problem dealt with in the following paragraphs is summarized in *Die Raum-Zeit-Philosophie des neunzehnten Jahrhunderts* (*The Space-Time Philosophy of the Nineteenth Century*) by Werner Gent, published by Friedrich Cohen, Bonn, 1930.

condition of our intuitions', or, in non-technical parlance, they are spectacles which we are already wearing before we look into the world and through which we necessarily see everything that affects our senses. The form of intuition then, according to Kant, is not an empirical concept 'deduced from outward experiences' and from which knowledge might consequently be derived by analysis. Space is rather an 'intuition *a priori*', which is found in us prior to any perception of an object. It lies 'prepared *a priori* in the mind' before we begin to have experiences. From this source of knowledge within ourselves we derive the axioms of Euclidian geometry. Modern physics contradicts this Kantian conception of space and maintains that space is not given us as 'pure intuition'. We do not know in advance what kind of structure space has, what its curvature is, and what dimensions it discloses. This can only be determined by astronomical and physical observation. Space then, say the modern physicists, flatly contradicting Kant, is 'derived from outward experiences'. Geometry is an experimental science. By purely empirical means the conclusion is reached that, for example, the cosmic space to which our solar system belongs is not Euclidian but spherical, i.e. like the surface of a ball, curving back to rejoin itself, even though this spherical curvature becomes perceptible only with measurements extending over very great distances.

Connected with this there is a second vitally important disagreement between Kant and a good many modern physicists. If, as Kant supposed, we derive the propositions of geometry from pure intuition, which lies ready prepared in our cognitive faculty prior to all experience, then there can be only *one* geometry, established once and for all and universally valid. But if geometry is an experimental science, we must reckon with the possibility that there may be various different geometries, based on various different axioms and yet, from the mathematical point of view, of equal validity. It is not for us ourselves to decide which geometry is applicable in a particular case. That will be shown by experience. In our encounters with reality it must be decided in each particular case which form of geometry is appropriate. It was the mathematicians who first laid the foundations for this new conception of space. Then the physicists took it up and developed it further.[1]

Euclidian space, which according to Kant is given *a priori,* rests, mathematically speaking, first and foremost upon the so-called axiom of parallels. If a point is given and a straight line, then only *one* straight line can be drawn through the given point and parallel to the given straight line. There is only *one* second straight line which lies in the same plane as the first and does not intersect it. During the eighteen-twenties the Hungarian Bolyai and the Russian Lobachevski more or less simultaneously discovered that, although it contradicts our intuition, it is mathematically possible to substitute for the Euclidian axiom of parallels a different axiom, according to which a number of straight lines can be drawn through a given point and parallel to a given straight line. It is quite as feasible to base a comprehensive geometry on this axiom as on the Euclidian axiom of parallels. Soon after this the German mathematician Riemann extended the concept of space beyond the space of the Euclidian system. Unlike Bolyai and Lobachevski he did not start out from the axiom of parallels but from the fact, already discovered by Gauss, that a curved surface, for example the surface of a sphere, may be treated as a two-dimensional plane. The figures which can be described on this surface may be represented mathematically by a process of analogy, just as are the plane figures on a surface within the Euclidian space, although of course there will be corresponding differences in the measurements. For example, the sum of the angles within a spherical triangle will amount to more than 180 degrees. The straight line, which for Euclid is the shortest distance between two points, is here replaced by the concept of the *straightest* line. These straightest lines are the great circles which pass through two diametrically opposite points. Consequently, they all intersect at the two points which represent the poles. And that contradicts the Euclidian axiom of parallels.

[1] Hans Reichenbach, *Philosophie der Raum-Zeit-Lehre (Philosophy of the Space-Time Theory)*, 1928.

All we have been doing so far is simply to start out from a two-dimensional plane and examine the way in which the measurements change on this plane if we replace the Euclidian surface by a spherical surface, which according to Euclid is curved, and treat this as a plane surface. In doing this we must think in terms of the consciousness of a being which lives only in two dimensions and for which the surface on which it moves has the measurements of a spherical surface. Up to that point we find no difficulty in conceiving all this graphically. But now comes the next step, which cannot be graphically represented. We must now transfer what we began by visualizing in the form of a two-dimensional surface to a three-dimensional space-structure. This space-structure differs from the entire Euclidian space with its three dimensions, just as the geometry of the two-dimensional *spherical surface* differs from the geometry of a two-dimensional *plane*. Just as the two-dimensional surface of a sphere curves back to rejoin itself, so too does this new stereometric space-structure. This goes beyond what can be graphically represented within three-dimensional space. We are confronted here with a space which has more dimensions than Euclidian space has. In the present context it is not possible for us to pursue any further mathematically the consequences which follow from this. It is enough if we have seen clearly that Riemann derives from it a concept of space which is far more comprehensive than the Euclidian concept had been. It is now possible to conceive of as many spaces as one pleases, all differing in their 'curvature'. Euclidian space is the space of which the curvature is nil. There are an unlimited number of other spaces with positive or negative curvature and in each of them the axiom of parallels assumes a different form. All these spaces possess equal mathematical validity.

The idea that three-dimensional space is merely one particular type of space among many possible types was expressed in literary form already thirty years before Einstein's theory of relativity by the Englishman Edwin Abbott in his story *Flatland*.[1] This tale was regarded at the time as an amusing *jeu*

---

[1] *Flatland, a romance of many dimensions, by A. Square,* by Edwin Abbott, 1884. Fourth Edition, Blackwell, Oxford, 1932.

I

d'esprit and was soon forgotten again. But in 1932, in the age of Einstein, it suddenly took on a new lease of life. In this story the starting-point for postulating more than one space is not, as it had been with the mathematicians we have mentioned, the axiom of parallels or the ratio of curvature, but a simple analogical inference, inferring from Euclidian space to spaces with more dimensions by the same process by which one may pass from uni-dimensional space to two-dimensional space and from there to three-dimensional space. We may start from the original state in which there are not yet any dimensions at all, i.e. from a consciousness consisting in a single point which possesses neither length nor breadth nor height. This point is self-contained. It is its own 'one and all'. 'There is nothing which is not within it.' When this original point is moved, it makes a line with its movement and so produces uni-dimensional world, Lineland, in which there can be only a succession of sensations, e.g. of sounds, but still no juxtaposition. If this straight line is now moved sideways it makes a square surface with its movement, and thus produces the two-dimensional Flatland. This is the world which the fictitious author of the story inhabits. All the inhabitants of Flatland are plane figures, animated triangles, polygons, circles, etc., living in houses which have lines for walls, and forming with one another the most varied relationships, which are amusingly described in the course of the story. If the square formed by moving the line is itself moved upwards, just as the line has been moved sideways, it produces a cube. This gives us Spaceland, with the three dimensions in which we ourselves live. Once we have taken these three steps, which have led us from the point to the line, from the line to the plane, and from the plane to the solid, we cannot possibly stop there and remain content with the state which we have thus achieved. The analogical argument, which is after all in all fields of study the key to new discoveries, compels us to consider carrying still further the process which has led us step by step to three-dimensional space. We must therefore assert that, if we move a cube just as we moved the square by which it was produced, there must arise out of the three-dimensional space a higher, four-dimen-

sional figure, a figure which does not, like the cube, possess
a mere eight corners, but sixteen. Just as the interior space of
the cube was bounded by six square surfaces, so the interior
space of this higher structure will have to be bounded by a
correspondingly higher number of cubes. And if this four-
dimensional figure is moved, it will necessarily produce a five-
dimensional space in the same way. And so on *ad infinitum.*

Thus, by this method of drawing analogical inferences,
though in a more primitive form than with the manipulation
of the axiom of parallels and the alteration of the ratio of
curvature, the one Euclidian space, the geometrical structure
of which, according to Kant, has been imposed upon us, prior
to all experience, as the unique and inescapable space pattern,
is replaced by a multiplicity of possible spaces, of which
Euclidian space is only one particular specimen.

The question now arises: Does this refute and invalidate
Kant's conception of space? Has geometry ceased to be an
a priori science which, like logic or algebra, establishes necessary and universally valid propositions? Has it become an
experimental science, like chemistry or biology, which can
only summarize results of observations and experiments? Or,
to express it in another way, does the source from which we
derive our knowledge of the structure of space lie in ourselves,
i.e. in the epistemological subject, or does it lie outside us, in
the object of our experience of the world? This question has
given rise to a dispute which has still not been settled between
the partisans of the neo-Kantian philosophy and the younger
physicists, and if we wish to define our attitude to it we must
start out from the point about which there is still some
measure of agreement between Kant and modern physics.
Modern physics, as can be seen for example from Heisenberg's
relation of indeterminacy, has been recognizing ever more
clearly that physical facts cannot be completely described or
exactly defined at all without including the cognitive subject
in the definition from the very outset. In reaching this conclusion modern physics has provided a surprising confirma-
tion of the Kantian critical principle that there is no objective
experience which is not the experience of a subject whom
reality objectively confronts. The ego and the object can

indeed be distinguished from one another by means of an abstraction, but they cannot be concretely detached from one another. If we eliminate the ego, and with it the whole underlying relation between subject and object, then, according to Kant, we are left with an unknown quantity, the 'thing in itself', about which no proposition can be asserted, and which is indeed merely an expression for the insurmountable boundary of all our human knowledge.

But if this Kantian principle is simply confirmed from another angle by modern physics, then the two quantities we are discussing, the knowing subject and the known object, are not by any means two separable entities either of which can be considered in isolation from the other. What we have before us is, on the contrary, always only a *relation* in which these two quantities stand to one another. Neither of the two quantities can be taken out of this relation. Consequently subject and object stand in the same relation to one another, figuratively speaking, as do the positive and negative poles, the *relation* between which produces the electric current. But if the subject and object cannot be isolated from one another at all as separable quantities, then the entire dispute between the physicists and the Kantians rests on an error in the posing of the problem. It is quite meaningless to ask whether the subject carries within himself the structural law of space or whether this is contained in the object. If someone is sitting in a room with walls which look blue, then one may certainly ask whether the walls themselves are painted blue, or whether the blueness arises only from the blue spectacles he has resting on his nose. This question is meaningful because the man's body and the wall of the room are two quantities which can be described in mutually exclusive terms. It is quite a different matter with the subject and the object. These, as we have seen, can only be distinguished from one another 'dimensionally'; they cannot be defined in mutually exclusive terms or isolated. They exist always in an indissoluble relationship with each other. The subject to which we are here referring is not the human being sitting in his room surrounded by things which confront him objectively; it is the ego, which must be clearly distinguished from the human organism with which it is linked by destiny. Indeed, as Rickert has demonstrated, this human body, together with all the notions and memories, the joys and sorrows which accompany its active and passive life in this world, is not the subject of which we are speaking here; it pertains rather to the object, by which the subject is confronted. It is a part of the objective world, the part of it to which my ego (if the body in question is my own) is linked by its destiny. If we take the ego in this pure, non-objective sense of the word, then the object and the subject can be differentiated only by means of an abstract distinction. They cannot be detached from one another concretely. Consequently, we are in reality always concerned only with the two together, i.e. with the peculiar *relation* in which they stand with respect to each other. One cannot, therefore, ask whether the structure of space has its origin in the subject or in the object. Space can always arise only from the totality of the subject-object relation. The form of the question must therefore be: What is the significance of space in making this relation what it is?

In order to answer this question we must revert to what was said in an earlier chapter about the objective world as the medium between the I and the Thou. The objective world was there compared with an opaque party-wall between two prison cells, which is peculiar in that it does not, like an ordinary prison wall, possess only two sides, enabling the prisoners in two adjacent cells to make themselves understood to each other by knocking on it, but innumerable sides, enabling an unlimited number of prisoners to establish communication with one another. The objective world as a whole is therefore the sum of the innumerable world aspects that reality presents to the many subjects which perceive it from the most extremely varied angles.

What rôle then, in the production of one of these many different world aspects, is played by a space in which reality appears to us? What is the significance in this connexion of any particular space, for example the Euclidian space which is allotted to us, who are talking together here, as the space in which we perceive objects? It seems to me that there is only one possible answer to this question. A space with a particular structure is the form in which the whole of reality, or else a part of it, presents itself to a particular subject, or else to a group of particular subjects, with which this reality, enters into a relation. To each subject, without any action on the part of this subject, there is assigned, already when it enters into its existence, a particular position in the objective world, as the centre of vision for its world picture. There is an obvious connexion between this centre of vision at which the subject finds itself situated, the standpoint from which it must observe the panorama of the world, and the space which for us, standing at this position, is the only possible form of perception in which we can see this reality. If we stood at some other position, if we had been born, not as human beings, but, for example, as blind moles, then the same reality would appear to us, but in a different aspect, and consequently perhaps in a quite different spatial form. But if we see this reality, for instance the galactic system to which our sun belongs, in this particular spatial form of perception and not in a space with a different curvature, that also follows, if we look at it from the other point of view, from the essential nature of the reality which here confronts us. It is an essential characteristic of this reality that it presents to such beings as ourselves precisely this aspect of itself which we perceive.

In order to make this situation clear, let us add to the simile of the prison wall yet another analogy which will illustrate the matter from another angle, an analogy drawn from the life of the mind. Let us consider a book, for example, which belongs to world literature and has therefore been translated into all the more important world languages, e.g. Goethe's *Faust*, the *Baghavadgita* or the Bible. To each one of us the content of this book is really accessible only when it is translated into our mother tongue. The content of the book, in isolation and apart from any kind of linguistic expression, is an inconceivable 'thing in itself'. Now each one of us, being bound by destiny to a particular position in the world of experience, is thereby given the space in which, viewed from this position, the world is perceptible to him. This is, as it were, the mother tongue in which reality becomes familiar to him, speaks to him directly and strikes his

connected with the fact that all of us alike, in our combined efforts to explore the world, are fated to be human beings and to have the centre of vision of our world picture in human bodies. The fact that we are thus situated in a particular position means that it is our destiny not to be inhabitants of the Flatland or Lineland or Pointland of which Abbott speaks in his story, but beings of the three-dimensional Spaceland. This pattern of being, which is given us when we enter into our existence, includes those primary axioms which are 'self-evident' for us because it is only when we apply them that the world becomes intuitively perceptible. That is the grain of truth in the Kantian doctrine of the spatial *a priori*. Euclidian space does not, therefore, arise from that element of our ego which, in our first chapter, we called the '*constant* element', the element which is still independent of the situation in the world of experience with which we are linked by our destiny; but it is nevertheless partly conditioned by the *variable* element of our existence, namely the destiny whereby we are 'cast' into precisely this situation in the world and put to work at this point.

It is true that Hans Reichenbach expresses the opinion that it is merely a matter of habit if it is only Euclidian space, and not, for example, a spherical space, which appears to us as the form of our perceptions. He thinks that if we were to occupy ourselves long enough with a spherical space, we should finally be able to accustom ourselves to the dimensions of this space and to adapt our vision to it so completely that in time we should accept this space as our form of perception, just as we now accept Euclidian space. But this suggestion, which Reichenbach puts forward in his *Philosophy of the Space-Time Theory* to which we have already referred, is scarcely convincing. For even if it were possible for us to accustom ourselves to a space with a curvature diverging only slightly from our own, it is still in any case quite out of the question that we, with the power of imagination that we possess, should be able to conceive of ourselves as living in a space with more than three dimensions, a space in which, therefore, more than three straight lines can be perpendicular to one another. The very fact that nowadays we can calculate algebraically with more than three dimensions, and deduce them from our theories of physics, makes it all the more understandable to us that Kant should have insisted that the world was perceptible to man only to the extent to which it passes before him in the one-dimensional time series and confronts him in the three-dimensional solid space. For the progress of mathematics and physics impels us, whether we like it or not, to fly away on the wings of the poetic imagination out beyond the frontiers of Euclidian space, and to attempt to conceive a space in which more than three co-ordinates can stand perpendicularly to one another. But all such endeavours to fly out beyond our frontiers always end only with our falling back with singed wings on to the ground of our Euclidian three-dimensional space. If we try to carry further the progression which leads us from the uni-dimensional time series to the line and from there to the two-dimensional plane space and from there to the three-dimensional solid space, if we try to take one step further and to attain to a multi-dimensional space, we encounter an insurmountable obstacle, an electrically charged barbed-wire fence, so to speak, which hurls us mercilessly back into our proper limits. Whatever we may do, however much we may exert our poetic imagination, we shall always come to the following negative conclusion. We can certainly *calculate* with spaces possessing more dimensions than the uni-dimensional space of time, or the three-dimensional solid space, or the combination of the two, the four-dimensional space postulated by Minkovski. But we cannot *conceive* these multi-dimensional spaces. Our power of *intuition* is confronted here by an insurmountable barrier. This makes us acutely and profoundly conscious of the correctness of Kant's assertion that 'we cannot judge at all whether the intuitions of other thinking beings are governed by the same conditions which limit our own intuitions' and his insistence on the other hand that for us 'dependent beings confinement within these two forms obtains universally'.

Indeed the special significance of the story *Flatland* lies precisely in the fact that it demonstrates clearly that we are confined within the space in which we find ourselves when we enter into our existence, as though in a prison from which we cannot escape. The inhabitants of Flatland can, of course, as the story says, *believe* in a third dimension. They may, like the fictitious author of the tale, allow themselves, for the sake of this belief in the third dimension, to be sentenced by the supreme court of the Flatlanders to lifelong confinement in a prison or a lunatic asylum. They may also dream of this more comprehensive space. But they cannot *see* it.

12. THE DISCLOSURE OF A NEW SPACE

To summarize the conclusion to which we have been led by all our considerations so far, it has become apparent on the one hand that it is our inescapable destiny that objects should become perceptible to us only within the pattern of Euclidian space, and yet, on the other hand, this Euclidian space itself shows us that there is not only one space but a multiplicity of spaces. For Euclidian space itself contains at least two partial spaces, the uni-dimensional linear space and the two-dimensional plane space. Moreover it follows from a mathematical consideration of the axioms and of the curvature of our Euclidian space that it is perfectly possible to posit spaces with completely different structures from those of the spaces which are contained in our intuitional space. This leads us to the idea that there are spaces which, although we cannot conceive them intuitively, still possess structures which can be adequately expressed in algebraical terms. Reality is evidently very much richer, deeper and more mysterious than it at first appears to us to be. Even the entire objective space, which we are able to explore with the telescope and the microscope, is only one aspect of the world amid many possible aspects. But if we have to reckon with a multiplicity of spaces in which the contents of the world may be arranged according to different principles of classification and different structural laws, then clearly there are four possibilities.

Firstly, a space may, like our Euclidian space, be entirely disclosed to intuitive perception and geometrical formulation.

Secondly, it may be that a space which we cannot visualize

is still comprehensible if we generalize and manipulate the axioms of our intuitional space in such a way that they can be applied, in a figurative sense, to a space which is not intuitively perceptible to us. This is the case with the spaces which Riemann postulates.

Thirdly, a space may possess a structure which cannot be mathematically formulated at all, because this space lies completely outside the entire objective world. And yet this may still be a space in the true sense of the word, because in it too a multiplicity of entities are arranged in order according to a definite principle. We have an immediate knowledge of this principle, just as we have of the axioms of Euclidian geometry, and its universal validity appears to us to be equally self-evident. This is the case with the non-objective space in which encounters take place between subjects. Each one of us is directly cognisant of it. The existence of our own non-objective I and the nature of the non-intuitive encounter with a Thou: these are better known to us than the entire objective world that stands before us. The existential propositions which Heidegger asserts concerning our 'existence' (*Dasein*) and 'co-existence' (*Mitsein*) are certainly not intended to be considered as merely the personal experiences of an individual. They claim to be universally valid structural laws and principles of arrangement, which anyone who stands in the non-objective space will immediately see to be self-evident. The universal validity of these principles according to which our existence is ordered does not depend upon whether you or I or any other people have already become conscious of these structural laws or whether we have never before given them a thought and are only now having to have our attention drawn to them by existential philosophy. There follows from this a consequence which is of crucial importance for the philosophical significance of the problem of space. We may be situated in a space, and pass every instant within that space, and yet the time has still to come when our eyes will be opened to the fact that we have always been living in this space. If our imagination and our thought have at first been entirely restricted to the one space of the primitives, and then later, as occurred in India at the time of the Vedanta and

again in Greece at the time of Plato, there is disclosed to us,
under the impact of grave upheavals disturbing our whole
existence, a new and hitherto unknown space in which we
exist, then we know from the very first moment that this
newly discovered space has not just come into being at this
particular moment; we know that we and all other beings,
without exception, have always been surrounded by this space,
although until now we have been blind to it.

Fourthly, it is also possible that a space may lie altogether
beyond the range of what we can see or infer mathematically,
even beyond all the spaces in which we stand existentially
without ever yet having become conscious of it. As we saw
in the chapter entitled 'The Psychical Content of the World',
even when we consider the life of the plants we begin to
realize that these beings have a completely different time scale
from our own. This suggests the idea to us that even outside
the human world there may be psychical beings which see
reality from quite a different angle from our own. We must
therefore from the outset be prepared to accept the possibility
of beings which live in a space pattern that is completely inaccessible to us.

When, under the impulsion of modern physics and the new
trend in mathematics since Riemann, we have extended the
concept of space in this way, there is still one final question
to be elucidated which is of fundamental significance for all
the rest of our discussion. If, as we have seen, we can be
situated in a space without being aware of it, that is to say if
this space has at some time still to be disclosed to us, this
leads us to the question: How can we tell in a particular case
that what has been revealed to us is indeed a new space and
not merely some hitherto undiscovered region of the cosmic
space we knew already? If a new continent comes into view,
as it did when America was discovered, or if an astronomer,
using the gigantic telescope of the Mount Wilson observatory,
descries a new galactic system which had hitherto been hidden
from human eyes, this is seen to be new because it is not yet
marked on our charts and maps, because, in other words, it
lies out beyond the frontiers within which our experience of
the world had hitherto been confined. Nothing of this kind

can happen with a space; for, of course, a space has no frontiers at all. A space may indeed be finite, like the spherical space, for example, which curves back to rejoin itself, but it is still without boundaries. And if, according to the view of some contemporary physicists whom we shall be discussing later, it is matter which 'tenses' a space of a particular structure, this space is still not confined by the matter which produces it, in the sense in which the extension of a fluid or the expansion of a gas is confined by the walls of a retort in which these liquid or gaseous materials are enclosed. For even though a space may stand in a relation of physical dependence with respect to matter, this does not mean that it has itself become a material the expansion of which can be restricted by material resistances. If we wander or fly through a space, through Euclidian space for example, we never encounter a fence or a wall which indicates to us that space goes so far and no further.

But if a space is certainly not limited in the sense that we encounter a material obstacle which makes us clearly aware that it stops at a definite place, how then can we become conscious of the limits of this essentially limitless whole? How can we tell that beyond this whole there is something else, namely a new space of which we have so far been unconscious? It is, after all, impossible for something to break into a space from outside, as the sunshine breaks through the clouds and lights up a landscape which, until then, had been veiled in misty greyness. For a space, in the sense in which we are here using the word, is not, of course, a self-contained totality with an exterior covering in which holes might be torn from outside. It is, on the contrary, open on all sides and not confined within any material walls. How, in these circumstances, can a new space manifest itself? There is only one possible way. Let us first of all consider the axiom of parallels within Euclidian space, and the change which occurs if, for Euclidian space, a spherical space is substituted. That this substitution has taken place becomes clear to us when we encounter a straight line (i.e. a great circle of the spherical space) to which no parallel straight line (i.e. no parallel great circle) can be drawn through any point whatever without intersecting it, always at the same point.   On the Euclidian plane that is a contradiction, an invalidation of one of the fundamental axioms upon which Euclidian space is built up. The existence of a new space is consequently demonstrated by something being an undeniable fact while at the same time representing a contradiction within the space which was hitherto known. In the second space something is possible which within the first space was contradictory.   This is the sign whereby a new and hitherto unknown space may manifest itself.   This is what shows that there is something which lies beyond the limits of an essentially limitless whole.

We can visualize this most rapidly if, like the author of *Flatland,* we begin by putting ourselves in the position of a being which is confined to a uni-dimensional space of time, a being to which the plane and solid worlds are still unknown, since its entire experience takes place solely within the one dimension of the succession of events in time.   In the time series as such there is nothing but a *succession* in which impressions follow after one another.   Let us suppose, for example, that we are listening to a violin solo which is so enthralling that it makes us forget completely that we are ourselves solid beings sitting amongst other solid beings in a concert hall and that the sounds are being produced on the platform by a solid instrument.   We have left the entire space of solid bodies behind us.   The world has transformed itself into music.   Reality has now only one dimension.   It has become a continuum of sounds which arise one after another as though without reference to space.   When, after the last chord has been played, we return from this musical experience to the three-dimensional space, which for a few precious minutes we had left entirely behind us, this return makes us conscious of what the transition from the space of time to two-dimensional space signifies if we consider it from the standpoint of an experience in pure time.   What does this transition signify?   What is disclosed to us when it takes place? We can answer this question only by saying that two entities contained in the time series, e.g. the notes C and E, must necessarily, within the uni-dimensional space of time, either *not* coincide chronologically, that is to say they must follow one another, in which case they remain separate, or else they *must* coincide in time, in which case they necessarily become one as to their contents, that is to say they merge in the chord C-E. There is no third possibility. All musical composition is subject to this restriction. But once the two-dimensional plane space is disclosed, this either-or, this bare alternative to which purely temporal experience was confined, is eliminated at a single stroke. A third possibility is introduced, which, from the standpoint of the time series, would have implied a contradiction. It is now possible for two entities to coincide in a single moment and yet to remain just as completely separate in respect of their contents as if they were succeeding one another in time. How is this made possible? It is made possible by the new relation of *juxtaposition* which can arise on a plane surface. Juxtaposition opens up an immense wealth of new possibilities. Even this quite elementary example illustrates the general principle that the emergence of a new and more comprehensive space is always heralded by the elimination of the opposition between two mutually exclusive alternatives; this opposition, which had been characteristic of the space hitherto known, is bridged over by the introduction of a third possibility. The two possibilities within which we were confined in the uni-dimensional time space were subject to the logical principle of the 'excluded third'. Once the two-dimensional plane is disclosed, this 'third', which within the time space was 'excluded', becomes an undeniable reality.

The same rule governs the transition from the two-dimensional plane to the three-dimensional solid space. This latter arises when, to the two dimensions of the plane surface, there is added a third dimension, that of depth, which at once makes our perceptions plastic and palpable. Whatever picture presents itself to our eyes, be it landscape or the interior of a room, we can see it at first purely as a surface, a juxtaposition of colours and lines, just as a painter records it on the two-dimensional surface of his canvas. It may be that a baby, reaching out its tiny hands for the moon, at first sees the world purely as a flat surface. But the same reality, with the same colours and outlines, suddenly assumes bodily shape, when,

as though everything were transformed by a great shock, the
dimension of depth is disclosed to us. Now there are two
spaces at once, in each of which everything is arranged in
order. We are still situated in plane space, but, at the same
time, a more comprehensive space has been disclosed to us, a
space of which plane space is a partial space. If we wish to
describe in terms of the old, two-dimensional plane space
what has now occurred, the emergence of a new and more
comprehensive space, then we must assert a paradoxical
proposition. We must assert that something is now possible
which within the plane space would be impossible and contradictory. If, in plane space, there are three points, A, B
and C, lying one behind the other on a straight line, and I
wish to proceed from A to C without passing through B, then,
within the plane, I am compelled to choose between two
possibilities. I must go round B either to the right or to the
left. But if solid space has been disclosed to me, then a third
possibility is suddenly made available, transcending the choice
which plane space offered me, transcending, that is to say, the
two possibilities which alone presented themselves within the
plane. I can proceed in a third direction and pass from A to
C by moving in a third dimension, either over B or under it.
In this way the bonds are broken which held me fast within
the plane space. In the story *Flatland*, this is demonstrated by
a guest from Spaceland visiting Flatland and being able to
disappear suddenly and to become invisible in a way which
seems to the Flatlanders to smack of uncanny wizardry. He
can pass through the locked doors of their houses, which have
lines for walls, for he can, of course, always move out into the
third dimension, to which the inhabitants of Flatland have
no access.

We can see from all these examples that, when a new space
is disclosed, there emerges a new reality which overcomes the
'either-or', the abrupt dichotomy, upon which the structure
of the previously known space was built up. There always
comes into play a new possibility, which, in the previously
known space, was the 'excluded third'. Approached in this
way, the final and most important space discovery is seen in a
new light; this is the discovery which, as we have seen, has

K

brought about a revolution in the entire history of thought, namely the discovery of the non-objective space in which the encounter takes place between the I and the Thou. This transition from the objective to the non-objective space is also subject to the same rule as were the transitions from the uni-dimensional space of time to plane space and from plane space to solid space. This shows particularly clearly that the non-objectivisable region which we encountered in our earlier chapters may also be termed a space in the extended sense in which we have already been employing this word. We can see that our position, the position at which, within the three-dimensional solid space, we encounter the invisible presence of the ego, which itself pertains to another space, this position is the centre of vision, the seeing point in front of which the whole panorama of the ever-changing three-dimensional world moves past as though on an illuminated stage. As we have seen already in an earlier chapter, this centre of vision of our world picture is peculiarly situated. It is part of the general objective picture, and yet it is itself invisible. The seeing point cannot see itself. I cannot view objectively this centre, from which alone the picture becomes visible. Consequently, if I wish to describe this centre of vision, I must assert two propositions which contradict one another. Firstly, this point pertains to the picture itself; it is an indispensable component part of the picture and has a quite definite position within it. Without it the picture would be incomplete. It is a part of it just as necessarily as the centre of a circle drawn on a blackboard is a part of the surface enclosed by this circle. And secondly, this centre is not part of the picture. For indeed it cannot be objectivised at all. Consequently, it lies completely outside the entire objective space. It has no location at all within the objective plane. It cannot be localized anywhere within it.

This paradoxical fact, which can be described only by asserting these two mutually exclusive propositions, has always been expressed by saying that the centre of vision is 'the blind spot' in our world picture. But that is merely a figurative expression for the irreconcilable contradiction which the centre of vision implies. If this point is a 'spot' within the picture, then it is an intrinsic part of the picture. But if it is a *blind* spot, then it is a place at which nothing at all can be seen, and consequently it lies completely outside the entire visible picture. Now we cannot, of course, form any picture at all of any part of the objective world, whether it be an extensive landscape we are viewing or a tiny organic cell which we examine under the microscope, without looking at it from our centre of vision. It is only from there that the elementary parts of which it consists are combined together, and without this centre of vision they fall apart. Thus, every act of seeing is an act of organization which is possible only from a point lying outside the entire objective world. In this act of visual organization, as has already been seen, two factors are always present together which, within the objective space, are mutually exclusive. A point is given which lies within the picture and yet, at the same time, outside the picture, because it does not pertain to the objective world at all. This paradox of the act of visual organization, which we perform every time we perform the act of seeing, demonstrates particularly clearly that we are always living in two opposing spaces. At every moment there is disclosed to us the new space, which stands outside the dimensions and structural laws of the objective world space, and which renders possible something that within the objective world would be impossible and self-contradictory.

The same mysterious synthesis of intrinsicality and extrinsicality which confronts us in the *here*, in the centre of vision, at which we look in, as it were, from a different, non-objective dimension into the objective three-dimensional space, this same mysterious synthesis confronts us also, in the uni-dimensional space of time, in the *now*. If we leave the ego out of account, then the time series, as we saw in our chapter entitled 'The Will and Events in the World', is nothing more than a sequence of successive moments, which might just as well be traversed backwards as forwards, and in which any one moment possesses the same importance as any other. The present moment too is carried away by the stream of time, and sinks into oblivion, making way for its successor. The picture changes completely if we look at time from the point of view of the ego. The present moment is now no longer a point of time which is carried away by the time-stream. The *now* acquires a special significance which comes to it from another dimension. It is, from the point of view of the ego, the *nunc aeternum*, the ever constant *now*, through which the stream of time continually flows. Just as the *here* lies simultaneously inside and outside three-dimensional space, so too does the *now* always lie simultaneously both inside and outside the time series. Since I am linked by my destiny to this present moment, I am, from the objective point of view, entirely carried away by the flying of time, and compelled to move with it incessantly; but from the other, non-objective point of view, I stand entirely apart from the stream of time. I look in, as it were, from another space into the space of time. The paradoxical double aspect of the *now*, the irreconcilable contradiction between the two assertions by which we have to express the essential nature of the *now*, this shows us that at this point too a new space is emerging. Within the objective region it can be formulated in terms of a contradiction. It bridges over the opposition between intrinsicality and extrinsicality, which in objective thinking are mutually exclusive. The fact that the non-objective ego-space renders possible something which on the objective plane would be a contradiction is apparent not only from the individual subject and its relations with the *now* and *here*, but also in the relations of a plurality of co-existing subjects. As we saw clearly in the chapter on the I and the Thou, the simplest Thou relation, which we experience every day, confronts us with a conflict between two sets of facts which we are unable to correlate, however much we may exert our imaginations. The conflict does not arise from the fact that the world can be seen not only from the one standpoint from which I now see it but also from the other standpoint from which the other person, who confronts me, sees everything. I can conceive of that without any difficulty; for I can, of course, at any moment by changing my location leave the place where I am standing now and move to another position from which the world looks different. But now comes the difficulty. When I change my standpoint in this way, *either* I stand here at point A, *or* I stand there at point B. In the latter case I have left point A. In either case the world has still only one centre. Now, the puzzle with which the I-Thou relation confronts me lies in the fact that, on the one hand, the mutually exclusive *either-or* still persists. It is *either* I *or* Thou. *Either* I am in the middle of the world, *or* you are at that centre around which everything turns. But, simultaneously with this, there is present between these two points of view a relationship of *both-and*. *Both* you *and* I, of course, always exist together simultaneously, and we see the world at the same time from two opposite standpoints. This means that the world has acquired two centres, both of which give it its direction simultaneously. The *or* relation and the *and* relation between the I and the Thou cannot be synthesized on the objective plane without involving a contradiction. All we can ever do is to alternate between the two mutually exclusive overall pictures. It is only by virtue of the non-objective space of the encounters between the I and the Thou that these two pictures can co-exist. Thus the situation here is similar to that which we shall later find in quite a different connexion when we consider the physical study of the elementary particles. There again experimental observation will confront us with two pictures which on the objective plane are irreconcilable, the corpuscle picture and the wave picture. But the fact that the two contradictory aspects are 'complementary', and together form a higher unity, indicates that perceptual space is not adequate for the representation of this situation, and that, in order to explain it, we must have recourse to non-perceptual dimensions which can be expressed only in mathematical terms.

Similarly, the existence in the Thou relation of two irreconcilable perceptual pictures indicates the existence of a non-perceptual space in which something is possible which in the perceptual space would be impossible. It becomes evident here that not only does the individual ego, as Fichte recognized already, stand apart from the whole objective world as the non-objectivisable subject, but also the manner in which individual subjects enter into relations with one another pertains to the non-objective space. If we wish to express this in a logical form, we must assert that in the space hitherto known

we are confronted with a simple choice between two possibilities, a choice which is governed by the strict rule that 'a
third is not given', *tertium non datur*. That which in the
space hitherto known was the 'excluded third' is in the new
space 'not excluded'. It is included in the extended range
of dimensional possibilities which this new space contains
within itself.

III

GOD, THE EGO AND THE WORLD

13. THE COSMIC FORM OF POLARITY

Everything that has been said so far, everything that has been said about the three spaces in which we, together with the whole of reality, are situated, was only the preparation for the answering of the question: What is meant today when we utter the pregnant word 'God'? Today, as soon as the word God is uttered at all, two kinds of people part company. They are separated by a gulf which the vicissitudes that have befallen mankind during these last decades have rendered ever wider, deeper and more unbridgeable. The question used to be simply: Is there a God or is there no God? There were religious and anti-religious people, theists and atheists. Today, in the age of technology and great world wars, the rift has become much deeper. Today, in all civilized countries, there stands, on the one side, a mass, increasing on an ever more disturbing scale, of people who are not atheistic or anti-religious or anything of the kind, but who see no meaning at all in the whole question about which the atheists and theists used to quarrel, and who consequently view it quite dispassionately and without interest. They have no idea what the others are so excited about. And on the other side, as Pascual Jordan[1] says, there stand 'those who have remained objectively anchored and have themselves no understanding for this lack of understanding which they observe'. It is as though two people were looking up at the starry sky on a clear winter night. One of them points at a place in the sky

---

[1] *Die Stellung der Naturwissenschaft zur religiösen Frage* (*The Attitude of Natural Science to the Religious Problem*), by Pascual Jordan, *Universitas*, Vol. I, No. 5, p. 514ff.

where he sees a brilliant star which he is convinced is the central sun by which the whole cosmos is moved. But the other does not understand him at all; for however intently he fixes his eyes on the point in the sky which his companion has indicated to him, he could swear that there is nothing there, and indeed that there never can be anything there. This mutual incomprehension with which two groups of people confront one another today, this continual failure of each group to make itself understood to the other, is manifest when theologically trained people, from amongst those who are still religiously anchored, oppose the 'secularists', who stand on the other side, 'with the entire highly developed range of instruments of a music of which the secularized person is unable to grasp even single notes'.

If, in this peculiar situation, we wish to render at all intelligible what is meant by the word God, we cannot begin with any kind of *proof* of God. The majority of our contemporaries no longer have any idea at all what it is that a proof of God is intended to prove. Nor can we begin, as a theology with some particular ecclesiastical affiliation would do, by putting forward a highly developed and copiously expounded *concept* of God. This would be like 'trying to make an impression on someone who is ignorant of the rudiments of music by playing, for example, a Bach fugue'. What the present situation demands is rather that we should attempt something which Pascual Jordan calls for in the name of the natural scientists and which he sets up as an ideal, namely 'a translation of the content of the term, without any diminution of it, into the language of our own time, which cannot, after all, be anything but a scientific language'.

This translation must above all things render intelligible the puzzling fact that, when we utter the word God, we are in the presence of a reality which, for the minority, for those who are said to be 'religiously anchored', is reality *tout court*, the most real reality of all, the reality without which all existence becomes meaningless, the reality without which the ground would be taken away from under their feet, the reality without which life is not worth living; while the others cannot understand what this is all about, and what it is that is regarded by a certain group of people, few in number but in some cases very eminent, as the *ens realissimum*, the most real reality of all.

In order to render this intelligible, we must set out from that comprehensive view of the world of experience which we obtained in Section I. We discussed the contrasting structures of the two spaces, both of which comprise the whole of reality, and in both of which we are all always simultaneously situated, the non-objectivisable space in which encounters take place and the objective space of the two spatial-temporal forms of intuitive perception. From this it can be seen that, despite their completely opposite structures, these two spaces nevertheless have one vitally important fundamental characteristic in common. Both the succession of occurrences within the time series and the juxtaposition of objects in three-dimensional space, as well as the completely different antithesis between the I and the Thou in the space which cannot be objectivised, are alike governed by one fundamental law, a law which is found again in all these relations in ever new variations. The two members in the relation are always linked in such a way that they are mutually exclusive and yet mutually dependent. A excludes B, and yet without B there can be no A. The equilibrium of A can be maintained only with B as its counterpoise. The wise men of the Eastern Asiatic world, the teachers of the world-famous *Tao To King* (*Tao and its Effect*) and of the *Yi King* (the *Book of Transformations*) designated this primary law, which governs all the relations we have so far considered, with the word Tao, which cannot be rendered in our European languages. In the period before the penetration of Buddhism into China, the term Tao comprised the whole of religion, ethics and political philosophy, and the whole of natural philosophy as well. It was like a single infinitely profound archetypal word, in which the whole mystery of existence appeared to be contained. We experience this law most directly in the daily alternation of daylight and night, which exclude one another and yet are the condition of each other's existence; in the relation between parents and children; and especially in the antithesis between the male and female sexes, which cannot exist without one another. We find this law in all earthly relationships, in ever new variations.

This primary law, to which everything is subject, may be represented symbolically by painting a circle on the wall and drawing a double curve inside it like that of a large S, starting from the periphery of the circle at the top and ending at the opposite point at the bottom. This produces the figure which we all know from Gothic tracery, consisting of two 'fish bladders', one with its thick end upwards and the other with its thick end downwards. In China every coolie knows this mysterious sign.

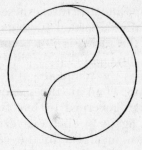

If we meditate upon this profoundly symbolical figure, it affords us a single comprehensive view of the secret of the world better than many words and philosophical speculations could give. The two 'fish bladders' are oppositely orientated. In other words, they conflict with one another. And yet, precisely because of this opposite orientation, they are complementary to one another and counterbalance one another. This is indicated by the fact that they are enclosed together within a circle, so that there arises a form of harmonious beauty, of which the Gothic architects have repeatedly made use. According to the wisdom of the Far East, which epitomizes the mature fruit of the experience of life amassed by the greater part of mankind in the course of thousands of years, we give our existence its proper meaning only if, in all the relationships of our life in the human community, in the family, in the law, in the state and in politics, we live in conformity with Tao.

The archetypal word Tao, which cannot be rendered in our

European languages, implies in the first place the fundamental recognition of the fact that all relationships in the
world, both in nature and in the personal life, rest upon a
single archetypal relation, an archetypal sound (*Urklang*),
which we must repeatedly strain our ears to hear in everything which is around us and in us, and which continually
returns in countless variations. All the relationships in the
world of experience in which we live are always only new
variations on this one theme. The archetypal relation of Tao
is so pregnant and profound that it can always be developed
in some new direction. For the Eastern Asiatic world of Taoism, the most important aspect of immersion in this archetypal relation was the balance of tensions, that is to say the
deep repose in eternal movement, which has perhaps found its
most beautiful expression in Goethe's famous verses which run :

> When in the infinite the same
> Flows eternally, renewing itself,
> When the thousandfold vault
> Mightily enfolds itself,
> Joy of living pours from all things,
> From the smallest and the greatest star,
> And all jostling, all wrestling,
> Is everlasting rest in God the Lord.

For Western thought, to which Hinayana Buddhism forms
the transition on the Asiatic side, it is the other aspect of the
Tao relation which assumes the greatest prominence when
this archetypal mystery is contemplated, namely the eternal
movement which this archetypal relation produces, the restless flight of time, such as Hölderlin has represented it in his
Song of Fate, as the fundamental characteristic of our entire
human existence.

> But to us it is given
> To rest nowhere.
> Mortal men
> Sink and fall,
> Like water hurled
> From cliff to cliff,
> For years, into the uncertain.

In contrast to the still, self-contained world picture of the Tao symbolism, there accordingly arises in the West the 'Faustian' impulse, striving in restless movement towards the infinite.

With speculative idealism, and especially with Schelling, the Eastern Asiatic Tao sign was superseded by a new analogy, representing a certain synthesis between the *balance of tensions,* whereby, according to the Eastern Asiatic emotional attitude to life, the two members involved in the opposition held one another in equilibrium, and the flow of unresting, unceasing, Faustian *movement,* which corresponds to the Western emotional attitude to life. This analogy is the relation, at that time newly discovered, between the positive and the negative pole, both of which must be present if the electric current is to circulate, in other words the relation of *polarity.* But whichever symbol we may select, whichever aspect of the cosmic mystery may acquire the greatest prominence, whether we call it Tao or polarity, it is always one and the same inexhaustible and unfathomable archetypal relation, recurring in ever new forms in every cosmic relationship, in the encounter between the I and the Thou as well as in the time series and in three-dimensional space. Consequently, however much their structures may differ in detail, all the experiential spaces we encountered in the last chapter may be considered together as one single space, which we may call the space of polarity or the *polar space.*

This fundamental law of polarity governs, in the first place, the relationships of the spatial-temporal world of objects. Let us first consider the time series. A point of time, for example the moment in which we now stand, is not in itself, simply by being there, capable of occupying this particular position in the time series. It has acquired this position solely by dint of following another point of time, one which has just elapsed, and by dint of preceding another point of time, one which is still to come. Consequently, within the polar space, there can be no beginning and no ending of time. For every point of beginning must be the point of ending of a preceding length of time, and every point of ending must be the point of beginning of an ensuing length of time. From this it follows that the cosmic process can have no ultimate cause and no ultimate goal. For every cause is the effect of preceding causes and every effect is in its turn the cause from which new effects proceed. Consequently, there is no origin of the world and no perfecting of the world. The cosmic process is an unceasing movement, a journey with no point of departure and no destination.

What must be said of the point of time must also be said of the point of space. Let us consider a point in the infinite and completely empty cosmic space. This point in itself has no location in space. It is, so to speak, everywhere and nowhere. It acquires a definite position in the three-dimensional solid space only when at least one other point in space is also given, beside it or above it or below it, a point with respect to which it stands in a spatial relation. It is only relatively to this second localized point that it acquires a particular location in space. It is the same with the relation of rest and movement. A solitary point in the midst of an infinite space cannot be said either to be at rest or to move. The distinction between rest and movement arises only when at least two bodies, A and B, are given. Point B may then be in motion relatively to Point A, if B is moving away from A; or B may be at rest relatively to A, if A is moving away from B; or both points may be in motion relatively to each other, or both may be at rest relatively to each other, if their distance from one another remains constant. It is the same with all quantitative relations in space. The size of a body or the length of a line can always be determined only if a definite scale is available by which they are measured and relatively to which they therefore have a definite extension. An illustration is afforded by the standard metre in Paris, which provides the basis for all metrical measurements.

But it is not only these elementary relations of the spatial-temporal objective world that are governed by the law of polarity. The non-objective relations too, which are present within the polar space, are subject to the same fundamental law. For, as we saw in the chapter entitled 'The Encounter with the Thou', I am I only by virtue of not being you or anyone else. It is the condition of my existence as 'I' that I occupy this situation to which I am linked by destiny and not the situation in which you stand and in which I might equally well be standing. In this quite elementary sense it is true to say that 'I am only by virtue of you'. I am myself only by dint of distinguishing and differentiating myself from you, just as a point occupies a position in space only by dint of standing in a relation of opposition to some other point. In the polar space, therefore, there is no ego existing in absolute isolation, by virtue of itself alone, and self-contained. On the contrary, the world of the I-Thou encounters resembles a chain, in which all the links afford one another reciprocal support, but in which one can discern no first and last links, such as might be attached to a ring on a wall, supporting the whole chain. Thus I, Thou, He, and so forth, form a chain which by its nature cannot have an end, a chain in which each link excludes the next and precisely on that account is supported by it and conditional upon it, a chain in which no first and last links are visible such as might ultimately support the whole. The non-objective Thou relation, too, is governed by the same law of polarity as are relations within the spatial-temporal objective world. Here too, as in the succession of points in the time line, there arises an incessant movement within an interminable series. Each I seeks its Thou, by which it is supported and yet always at the same time excluded and repelled. This 'other I' (*alter ego*), from which I must differentiate myself in order to 'find myself', itself in turn has need of a third, to which it stands in the same relation of dependence, and so on *ad infinitum*.

We could continue here and consider also, from the same point of view, the legal and ethical obligations under which we stand, showing in each case that these too, so long as we are restricted to the polar space, can never be anything other than links in a chain which has no first link and which never comes to rest in a final link. We intend to deal fully in a later chapter with these central obligations of our practical life. Our concern here has been only to devote a brief glance to the most elementary relations of our existence and thereby to make it clear that in fact all these relations are governed by the one all-predominant principle of polarity.

Tolstoy, in the prime of his life, at the age of fifty, was so affected by the discovery of this fact that his thought and work took an entirely new turn. In his book, *My Confession,* he describes vividly how, when his creative power and his worldly success were at their highest point, he was suddenly impelled to ask himself: What am I living for? When I have achieved everything I can achieve as landowner and author—what then? What purpose does it all serve? He had exchanged views with natural scientists and philosophers in his quest for an answer to this question regarding the ultimate meaning of our existence. He saw himself as a man lost in a forest, first climbing a tree in order to see where he is and then plunging into the undergrowth in the hope of finding a way out. What one sees from the tree-top is the world-picture of natural science, which is obtained by observation. The undergrowth is 'the darkness of the speculative sciences'. But in both cases he experienced the same disappointment. He was stand-ing alone in the midst of a boundless space. Everywhere there were series without beginning or end, lines of development leading forwards and backwards to infinity, an ocean of tree-tops stretching to the most distant horizon, but 'nowhere, no-where a house; dense undergrowth, in which I sank into ever thicker darkness the further I advanced and the more con-vinced I became that there was no way out and never could be one'. Overwhelmed by the realization that, in conse-quence of the polarity of cosmic space, neither science nor philosophy can lead us to a solution of the problem of the ultimate meaning of life, Tolstoy was now confronted with the problem of God.

14. THE SUPRAPOLAR SPACE

If all relations in the polar world can be reduced to a single cosmic formula, then all the problems of life and of knowledge of the world can be summed up in the single question: What is our attitude to the underlying principle by which this entire world is dominated? The Asiatic does not divide up the whole of reality, as we Europeans do, into separate fields, such as religion, morality, natural science, technology and medicine, each of which must be studied by experts who are alone competent in their various specialities. He is concerned on the contrary, in religion, philosophy and the study of nature alike, always only with our attitude to that fundamental cosmic order by which both nature and human life are governed. If Asiatic thought is correct in this, then we too are always ultimately concerned only with one question upon which opinions differ, a question which has evoked contradictory answers from which all the conflicts between the various religions and philosophies arise. The question is this: Is the polar world-form the only form of existence there is? Does not everything—not merely our human existence, but everything that was or is or ever might be—fall inescapably, once and for all, under this one cosmic formula? Or is there some other form of existence in addition to polarity? These are, in the first instance, the two possibilities between which we have to decide in principle. If we suppose the first possibility to be true, i.e. if we assume that there is no existence which does not have the form of polarity, then we may on the one hand *accept* this inescapable state of affairs and arrange our lives accordingly, i.e. we may do all we can in order to bring our lives into harmony with this cosmic law. That was done, in an Asiatic form, in Taoism, the whole ethical purpose of which was to live in accordance with Tao. It is being done, in a European form, in Nietzsche's nihilism, which accepts the world. Or, on the other hand, we may *reject* this sole form of existence. Then all that remains for us is to take flight from existence and return to nothingness. This rejection of the will to be is the negative consequence which Vedantism and, in a different form, Buddhism have drawn from the inescapability of the polar world-form. According to the Upanishads, that maturest fruit of the Vedanta philosophy, the purpose of all thought and of all mystical contemplation is the return from the world of multiplicity to 'otherlessness', to the point of indifference at which all oppositions are levelled out and merged. The mind is to become like a mirror in which no image is any longer reflected, one from which all the contents of the world are eliminated. ' Even as a falcon or an eagle, there in the aerial space, after flying around, wearily folds its wings and betakes itself to its roosting, so too does the mind hasten towards that condition in which it is asleep, feels no desire any more and sees no dream picture. . . . That is its essential form, in which, with its longing stilled, it is itself its longing without longing, and sundered from care.   Then the father is not a father and the mother is not a mother, the worlds are not worlds, the gods are not gods, the Vedas are not Vedas, the thief is not a thief, the murderer is not a murderer, the penitent is not a penitent; then there is immunity from good and immunity from evil; for the mind has overcome all the torments of its heart. . . . There is no other beside it, nothing which differs from it. . . . Because it has become one-ness, therefore it does not see, it does not hear, it does not smell, it does not taste. . . . For those who go this way there is no return to this earthly whirlpool—no return.' This flight into nothingness, this attempt to be no more than a mirror from which all the reflected images have vanished, or an 'ocean into which all the rivers run and disappear, abandoning their several names and forms', can succeed only if our consciousness itself is extinguished after all its contents have been blotted out. This is in fact the only way that leads to liberation if our entire conscious experience is inescapably confined within the polar world-form.

A second possibility is present only if one assumption is made, namely that the polar form of existence is not the only one possible, but that there is a second, completely different mode of being in which the whole world-form of polarity is transcended, yet not by the blotting out of the entire contents of the world but by the recasting of them in a new form. If this second form of being is found, in which the polar form is not negatively but positively overcome, then it is not sufficient for this purpose that this second form of being should merely stand behind us as a paradise lost or lie before us as a wishful dream. Nor must this second form of being hover high above us in spatial transcendency merely as a distant beyond, 'up there in heaven'. For indeed in all these cases the polar world in which we are confined is not really overcome. For then precisely the reality in which we live and which oppresses us on all sides would be excepted from the suprapolar form of

L

being. On this field of battle, where each one of us is wrestling with his destiny, the polarity within which we are confined would not be eliminated. It is eliminated only if this other form of being is just as all-present and all-embracing and just as inclusive of the whole of reality as is the case with the polar form of being within which we are confined. If that is really to be so, then the suprapolar form of being too must be a space, just as the polar world is a space, and just as the three-dimensional intuitional space which presses in upon us from all sides is a space.

This brings us to the second revolution in the history of human thought, comparable with the change wrought by Copernicus and still more fraught with consequences than was that first revolution, whereby Plato, and still more clearly Fichte, passed beyond the phase of primitive thinking and disclosed the second, non-objective space, in which the I and the Thou encounter one another. This second quasi-Copernican revolution is the discovery of the suprapolar space. This discovery is of crucial importance for the matter with which we are concerned in this entire book. For it is only if we are entitled to call the suprapolar region a space that it is really possible to accomplish what Pascual Jordan sets before us as an ideal, namely the 'translation' of the contents of faith 'into the language of our present time, which is after all bound to be a scientific language'. For it is only then that the religious person ceases, for those who think in terms of mathematics and physics, to be like one who speaks in tongues, that is in words to which the speaker himself attaches a meaning but which the listener cannot translate into his own language because he lacks the key. A concept has been found which bridges the gulf that gapes between the polar and the suprapolar zones. This is the concept of space, which is here applied to the suprapolar realm but is at the same time one of the fundamental concepts with which modern physics works.

But when even an attempt is made to bridge the gap between these two fields with the help of the concept of space in a way which might perhaps lead to a mutual understanding between natural science and religion, there arises from the very outset a serious objection on the religious side. The suprapolar space is indeed—as will subsequently become clearer—the space in which God is present for us. If the space of God is reduced to a common denominator with the space of this world, is that not a Titanic attempt by human thought to make itself master of God and to enmesh Him, who is after all 'the wholly other', in the net of our human concepts and categories? Does that not lead us to the apologetic method which arose from the principle of the *analogia entis,* that is to say from the idea that God is and the world also is, so that both fall within the same concept of being, from which it follows that from the being of the created world, which is after all a reflection of the Creator, the being of the Creator may be inferred?

The answer to this objection must be that precisely the opposite is the case. The idea that God is present for us in the suprapolar space is precisely the means of invalidating the proposition of the *analogia entis.* Indeed it is the only effective bulwark capable of warding off the peril with which our religious life is threatened by that seductive proposition, the *analogia entis,* that at first sight appears so extraordinarily convincing. How does it ward off this menace? A space, such as the three-dimensional space for example, is after all, as Kant already demonstrated in his space theory, not an *ens,* a being, a reality, a 'thing in itself'. It is, as was explained in our chapter entitled 'The problem of space in modern physics', a *relation* into which a reality enters with respect to me, the percipient subject. In that chapter we spoke of language as illustrating this relation, in that it is the means whereby a book enters into a relation with us, when, after appearing in a number of other languages, it is translated into our own. Just as the language is not the substance of the book itself, but the form in which this substance reveals itself to a certain group of readers, so too the suprapolar space, in which God is present for us, is not the reality of God itself. This ultimate reality remains that which is 'wholly other', totally incomprehensible and entirely inaccessible to our thought and observation. It confronts us neither as an object, in the way in which solid objects are disclosed to us, nor as a Thou, in the sense in which the I and the Thou confront one another in the polar space. When we speak of the suprapolar space, we cannot be referring to the eternal reality of God itself, but only to one aspect, a side which is turned towards us, the only side from which God can be accessible to us, to you and me, if He is willing to disclose Himself to us at all.

Yet the concept of the suprapolar space, which we are employing here, does not merely exclude the proposition of the *analogia entis*; it is, indeed, the only effective means of defence against the danger which this proposition implies. For, if the 'infinite qualitative distinction' between the temporal and the eternal worlds is not to be clearly defined with the aid of the concept of space, if we are not in this way to invest this distinction with a meaning which the thinking man can understand, then we can only speak of the ultimate dichotomy, in which we are involved, *either* in an esoteric language which is completely unintelligible to those who do not share our views, thus enshrouding the matter in a mystical haze, *or* in similes borrowed without exception from the three-dimensional solid space. That is what we are doing when we say, for example, that the eternal reality, which Goethe tells us we must revere, is what is *over* us; it is 'above' the terrestrial world; or, alternatively, it lies *beyond* this world; it 'transcends' it; it lies outside the frontiers of this world; whatever emanates from it drops 'down from above', like a missile striking the earth's surface and making a hollow space, a shell-hole.

Similes of this kind—and of course they are perfectly justifiable as such—all illustrate the opposition between time and eternity by comparing it with the relation between things situated within the objective space. But this means that, involuntarily, against the will of those who are drawing these comparisons, the two quantities which it is intended to contrast are themselves converted into objective quantities, standing above or alongside one another. Thus, in an even cruder form than in the case of the doctrine of the *analogia entis,* the mode of being of God and the mode of being of the world are placed on the same level and reduced to a common denominator. Until we have quite consciously taken our footing on the idea of the suprapolar space, all our conceptions and thoughts will be inescapably confined within the limits of Euclidian space and the Ptolemaic notion of a two-storey world. Not even the most forceful words we may employ, in order to express the immense contrast between the being of God, who dwells 'up there above the starry firmament', and the being of the world here below, will lead us a single step beyond this old world-picture which has been engrained in us from our childhood. Theology, then, has only two alternatives between which it must choose. *Either,* as has become customary since it ceased to associate itself with the Kantian theory of space, it must abandon completely the endeavour to clarify its conception of space philosophically; in which case it will relapse, quite involuntarily, into a stage less advanced than that achieved by Plato and German idealism in the study of this problem, in other words into the state of mind which is still that of the primitive tribes of Central Africa. Even if theology employs philosophical expressions, such as 'transcendence' and 'immanence', and talks about the 'metaphysical' background of the world, this philosophical veil still does not effectively conceal the primitive intuitional space with its upper and lower storeys. *Or else* theology must place itself quite consciously on the basis of the new 'thinking in spaces' which began in natural science already some decades ago. It is only then that the possibility will arise of imparting to the words 'supramundane', 'suprahistorical' and 'supernatural' a meaning intelligible even to one who, under the impulsion of the immeasurable dimensions of our present-day astronomical world-picture, has grown out of the mythological space-picture of the primitives and is no longer able to return to the primitive state of mind.

We have now seen clearly how very far-reaching are the consequences which follow from recognizing that the suprapolar region is a space. This brings us to the question: How did the discovery of the suprapolar space come about? Where in the history of thought do we find the first traces of this quasi-Copernican revolution? The peoples who lived in the primitive space-picture localized their gods at some lofty spot in the three-dimensional perceptual space, the only space which was available to them, for example on the summit of a great mountain, where sky and earth meet, such as Olympus or the 'Mountain of the Gods' in the Himalayas, which even today Indian penitents ascend on their knees. Or else they believed that our entire observable space possessed an upper storey, in which, high above the stars, there dwelt the celestial beings. Already in the Old Testament there emerges, as a presentiment of the coming revolution in the whole of religious thought, an idea which would have been incomprehensible for the primitives. It is the idea which already Solomon expresses in his prayer at the dedication of the temple, when he says to God: 'Behold, heaven and the heaven of heavens cannot contain thee; how much less this house that I have builded' (I Kings 8.27). This idea of the inescapable presence of God achieves its perfect form of expression in Psalm 139, which is one of the mightiest prayers that have ever been prayed, in the words: 'Thou compassest my path and my lying down . . . thou hast beset me behind and before. . . . If I ascend up into heaven, thou art there: if I make my bed in the world of the dead, behold, thou art there. If I take the wings of the morning, and dwell in the uttermost parts of the sea; even there shall thy hand lead me, and thy right hand shall hold me.'

On the island of Nias during the time of the first world war, an awakening, which is still remembered in Indonesia as the unforgettable 'great repentance', was brought about when an entirely primitive people, a savage tribe of head-hunters, quite suddenly and in a manner which even today cannot be explained at all in terms of the psychology of religion, were filled with the idea which is expressed in this psalm, so that the entire life of this tribal community was radically transformed. These simple people could express their new discovery only in spatial terms, by saying 'God is but a hand's breadth above me', that is to say, He is everywhere immediately and inescapably near. And yet, of course, they were still at the stage of the primitive space-picture, the stage at which there is still only this one observable three-dimensional space. And so, just like the psalmist in his prayer, they could still only say: While we are in this observable space, there exists incomprehensibly a power which is entirely unobservable and which nevertheless, just like this three-dimensional space, surrounds us on all sides, 'behind and before', and accompanies us wherever we may go. We cannot continue in the presence of this power if we do not order our whole life anew. Many of these naïve people were impelled by this profoundly disturbing idea to take refuge in the primeval forest, in the fond hope that in the dense woods they might escape from the power which everywhere, no matter where they walked or stood, was but a hand's breath above them. But all in vain. There too they ran straight into the arms of this uncanny power. And so a good many of them hanged themselves in the forest, in the hope that perhaps in this way they would elude this invisible reality which seemed to be accompanying them wherever they might go.

We can see from all this that already the men of the Old Testament, and, independently of them, primitive tribesmen becoming aware of the presence of God for the very first time, could always find only one form in which to express the mystery of the invisible divine omnipresence. This form is space. For only a space in which we are situated is really inescapable. We can escape from any reality, any person or any thing, which is contained within a space, simply by removing ourselves to another part of the space, where this person or thing is not present. It is only the space itself that we cannot escape. Go where we may, we shall still run into it. That is why there is no other form of expression for the presence of the inescapable God than space.

But this cannot be the three-dimensional observable space in which for the time being we find ourselves situated. For, as it says in the Old Testament, we cannot see God and live. It follows that there must be some second space, just as all-present as the three-dimensional space but completely unobservable. If we become conscious of this fact, then a 'space-discovery' has occurred, still more fraught with consequences than was the quasi-Copernican revolution which had previously led to the discovery of the non-objective I-Thou space. The 'thinking in spaces', to which the previous section introduced us, thus attains to its final fulfilment. All attempts

on the part of theology and philosophy to grasp intellectually
and to express in terms of language the beyond, the transcendent, the supramundane, the supernatural, the suprahistorical
and the more than earthly, are doomed to failure from the
very outset so long as this quasi-Copernican reorientation has
not been accomplished. Try as we may to find an adequate
expression for the beyond, so long as we think in terms of the
primitive space-picture all the analogies we may draw will
always only lead us back, as we have seen, to the mythological
conception of an upper storey in three-dimensional space,
lying out of reach, far away and high above us, a Cloud Cuckoo
Land which is of no use at all to anyone with a mathematical
and scientific training, or else we shall speak of the all-pervading nearness of God of which Paul is thinking when he quotes
from the poet Aratus the phrase: 'In Him we live and move
and have our being,' and Tersteegen too, when he says: 'Air,
that fills all; air, in which we soar for ever; ground and life of
all things.' But this brings us close to pantheism, which
identifies God with the universe; and in the idea that God is
beyond and above the world, the essential idea of the faith is
lost. These are the only two possibilities open to us, so long
as we remain within the observable space and borrow our
analogies from it. Within the observable space it will never
be possible to reconcile conceptually the two sides of the
matter with which we are here concerned, namely the absolute separation of God from the world and the all-pervading
presence of God. If two regions in the perceptual space are
infinitely distant from one another, they cannot at the same
time be extremely near to one another. The case is altered
only when we have taken the step leading to the discovery
from which the Bible always sets out.

Despite the enormous multiplicity of forms and the extravagant wealth of configurations which the polar world contains,
the Bible treats it as a unity in calling it, as a whole, the
'temporal', when it says, for example: 'The things which
are seen are temporal' (II Cor. 4.18). The incessant flight of
time is, for the Bible, the characteristic feature of the world
which is governed by the law of polarity. In opposition to this
polar space of temporality, including as part-spaces both the

objective, perceptual space and the non-objective space of the Thou relations, there stands the archetypal space of eternity or of the omnipresence of God. As we have seen, each space possesses a structure which is fundamentally different from the structures of all other spaces. Consequently, any two spaces are separated from one another by an immense gulf. We need only consider the antithesis between the ego-space and the objective space. And yet these two spaces belong so closely together that they can only be distinguished by means of an abstraction.

It is only when this mysterious law which governs relations between spaces is applied to the connexion between the polar and the suprapolar space that we can understand the paradoxical fact, to which the Bible repeatedly refers, that God, whom no man can see, and who, as the Creator, is distinguished from all created things by an infinite qualitative dissimilarity, is nevertheless at the same time, everywhere and at every point in the world, inescapably near. If what we have here is two spaces, each of which embraces the whole universe but each in a quite different aspect, then a clear meaning is given to Max Planck's dictum: ' Our impulse to gain knowledge demands a unified view of the world and therefore requires that the two powers should be identified with one another which are everywhere effective and yet still mysterious, namely the world order of natural science and the God of religion. This would mean that the Deity, which the religious person endeavours to conceive with the aid of his outward and visible symbols, is essentially the same as the power which is present in the laws of nature, the power which the enquirer's sense impressions to some extent make known to him.'[1]

But it is not merely the paradoxical ' identifiability ' of the two extremely different regions referred to here by Planck that becomes comprehensible only when we ' think in spaces '. The same is true of the fact from which we set out at the very beginning of this section, the fact which repeatedly troubles us in the present-day conflict of beliefs, namely that the world

[1] Max Planck, *Religion und Naturwissenschaft (Religion and Science)*, 1947, p. 33.

of God, the world in which he who believes and prays is rooted with every fibre of his heart, the world which alone remains when all earthly things fade away, 'the sweetest and the surest, the noblest of all treasures', the world which for the believer is infinitely more real than the whole visible world together, for secularist man this world is simply not there. For him it is no more than an empty phantom, and he could swear that there is nothing whatever behind it and never can be anything. One cannot help asking how it is possible that two human beings, both belonging to the same genus *homo sapiens,* should confront one another with such an absolute lack of mutual understanding. This too we can understand only if we 'think in spaces'. As we have seen, it is a peculiar characteristic of the relation between any two spaces that they belong inseparably together and yet each is hermetically sealed off from the other. Neither of the two spaces stands directly open with respect to the other in such a way that it can make itself immediately manifest within it.

It is true that we are all at every moment situated simultaneously in all the spaces which together constitute the 'universe of spaces' (*das All der Räume*); for whenever there is disclosed to us the existence of a space which had previously been concealed from us, we know from the very first moment that this space has not just come into being, but that it had always surrounded us without our noticing it. Yet, nevertheless, we are not ourselves able to force open the gate which leads to a space that has so far been closed to us. Whenever we experience the discovery of a space, this discovery always simply falls into our laps as a gift. It is a transformation which takes place in the depths of our existence and which we cannot ourselves bring about by force. It is as when one who has been born blind receives the gift of sight, so that a world with quite new dimensions is suddenly accorded to him as a boon from heaven. This is true already of the first space-discovery, the disclosure of the non-observable world of the subjective encounters. Fichte once said that when a child pronounces the word 'I' for the first time, after always having spoken of itself only in the third person, this is a greater and more far-reaching event than its bodily birth had been. Until now

it had been living only in the objective It-space. But now the
gate has been forced open which leads to a new space, the
world of the I. What is said here about the I-space is even
truer with regard to the final and decisive space-discovery, the
realization that, while we are encompassed on all sides by the
temporal world, we stand at the same time even now in the
midst of eternity and are enclosed within the archetypal space
(*Urraum*) of God. We cannot free ourselves by means of our
own reason or our own strength from the secularist state of
mind in which we are blind to the space of eternity and live
confined within the endless prison of the polar space. Some
event must supervene which we cannot ourselves bring about,
so that, as it were, the scales suddenly fall from our eyes, as
happened with the primitive people of Nias at the time of the
'great repentance', and we discover that 'God is but a hand's
breadth above us'; we cannot escape from Him; wherever we
may turn our steps, we run straight into His arms. Since this
elemental occurrence can, even for ourselves, always only fall
into our laps as a gift, we cannot lead other people to this
discovery by intellectual argument or pedagogical activity if
the space of God is still concealed from them. We cannot on
our own account determine the place or the time or the contents of this event; we are drawn in by it like a swimmer
caught in a whirlpool, so that at a single stroke our entire
conception of reality is fundamentally transformed and we
suddenly look at ourselves and the whole world around us
with new eyes.

We cannot in the present context discuss every aspect of the
new perspective which is opened up for us when we have
experienced this transformation. But one crucial point must
be emphasized here already which makes clear how significant
for our practical life is the discovery of the suprapolar space.
So long as we have not become aware that the presence of God
is a space, encompassing the whole of reality just as the three-
dimensional space does, so long, that is to say, as we can conceive the world of God only as the upper storey of the cosmic
space, so long will God's activity, too, always be a force which
effects earthly events only from above. We imagine it, for
example, as resembling the occasional flash of lightning which

emanates from a dark, lowering cloud, heavily charged with electricity, and strikes some particular place on the earth beneath it, or an 'invisible hand' which reaches down from above in order to change the course of happenings here below. So long as no such intervention from above takes place, so long as 'everything goes on quite naturally', no trace of God is to be observed. The cosmic process continues on its autonomous course in accordance with the laws of nature and the unalterable sequence of cause and effect. It is only primitive people, still living by the light of a magical conception of nature, who see interventions of supernatural forces everywhere, in all striking phenomena. The further man's knowledge of nature progresses in this age of technology, so that everything which was formerly considered miraculous receives a natural explanation, the more completely religious belief dies away. If even in this age there are still scientists who understand causal relations and yet nevertheless maintain a religious attitude in their approach to nature, that can only be because, in their hours of religious devotion, they repress their knowledge of nature and relegate it to their subconscious. It is only by means of this *sacrificium intellectus,* by this immolation of their understanding, that they are able to cling to their belief in the rule of supernatural powers. As soon as the scientific explanation of the world has finally become the common property of all, even this last remnant of mythological thinking will disappear.

That is how the situation today appears to the secularist, who, of course, can understand the declarations of faith of pious people only in the sense of the primitive space-picture, that is to say, mythologically. All this is changed at a single stroke, once it has become clear that the presence of God is not an upper storey of the one cosmic space, but a separate all-embracing space by itself, so that the polar and the suprapolar worlds do not stand with respect to one another in the same relation as two floors of the same house but in the relation of two spaces. As we have seen, in two spaces one and the same reality may be ordered simultaneously in accordance with two entirely different structural laws. One and the same occurrence in the world may manifest itself to us in two differ-

ent aspects. The complex of colours and lines, represented
by a landscape spread out before us in the sunshine, may
appear to us two-dimensionally, as a plane surface, as the
painter sees it when he projects it on to his flat canvas. Yet
the same complex of colours and shapes, without any alteration of its contents, will appear to us as solid and plastic when
the dimension of depth is added and we look at it three-
dimensionally, so that the parts of which it is composed stand
not merely beside one another but also behind one another.
The effectiveness of faith for our struggle with our destiny
depends quite definitely upon whether, in thus always involuntarily looking at things in two different ways, we must
have recourse to a *sacrificium intellectus,* or whether we can
do so with a clear scientific conscience. For faith gives us the
strength which we need in everyday life, not when it is sustained by miraculous occurrences breaking through the order
of nature—the significance of miracles will be discussed in a
later section—but only when one and the same occurrence, an
occurrence of which we fully understand the natural causes,
for example the course taken by a disease which leads to
certain death or the fall of a bomb which destroys a house, at
the same time in itself appears to us as an act of God, which
we receive directly from his hands. But this relationship,
which enables us to see two different aspects of one and the
same reality, is not possible between contents but only between two spaces in which the same contents are differently
ordered. Only thus can we understand the attitude repeatedly
adopted by the men of whom the Old Testament tells.

David has taken to flight after the revolt of Absalom.
Shimei curses him and throws stones at him, which is simply
a natural resurgence of the old hatred which had arisen
through the tribal feud between the house of Saul and the
house of David. But David says: 'So let him curse, because
the Lord hath said unto him, Curse David' (II Sam. 16.10).
The calamities which befall Job are all simply natural occurrences—the robbers' raid, the lightning which strikes his
flocks during the heavy thunderstorm, and the hurricane
which blows from the wilderness and breaks down the walls
of the house so that the inhabitants are buried under the

174 *Christian Faith and Natural Science*

ruins. But Job says: 'The Lord gave, and the Lord hath taken away; blessed be the name of the Lord' (Job 1.21). Or we may take from our own time a well-known example which shows the same attitude. Leading Seaman Gorch Fock, who distinguished himself in the Battle of Jutland, wrote in his diary a few months before his death: 'That sailor was right when he wrote to his mother: And if you should hear that our cruiser has sunk with all hands, do not cry. Even the sea, into which my body goes down, is simply the open hand of my Saviour, from which no power can wrest me.' The strength of the faith which reveals itself in these examples rests on the fact that it does not cling to supernatural occurrences, but that one and the same event, the natural causation of which is quite apparent, is at the same time, and as such, an act of God. The surging ocean, in which according to the law of gravity the man must sink, is the open hand of the Saviour who gathers him up. This belief is possible only when one and the same event, which in the polar space is subject to temporal causation, is at the same time ordered quite otherwise in the suprapolar space. It is only on this assumption that a thinking man is enabled to envisage the two aspects at once. If this philosophical basis is lacking, anyone with a mathematical and scientific training, perceiving the causal relations of natural occurrences, finds himself in a false position as soon as he attempts to apply his belief to practical life. This 'double-entry book-keeping' is an inner dishonesty, which at once leads to trouble when the belief is subjected to a severe test. We can see from all this that the 'thinking in spaces' of which we spoke in the previous section is not merely a philosophical *jeu d'esprit,* but a matter of crucial importance for our practical life.

15. RELATIVISM OR POSITIVISM

Everything that has been said so far has, in the first place, shown us one thing, namely that not God Himself but his omnipresence within the world is a space in the comprehensive sense in which we have been employing this concept throughout the book. We have seen that both the relation in

which the presence of God stands with respect to the polar
world and the manner in which the discovery of this suprapolar world comes about alike display the same characteristic
features which we have encountered in the case of all the
spaces that have so far been discussed. But all that this gives
us for the time being is the general conceptual framework, the
form into which the suprapolar world fits. This formal homogeneity of the suprapolar space with the spaces of the polar
world is, however, always restricted to its spatial character as
such, i.e. to the general form of spatiality in which the suprapolar world, like the others, confronts us. As soon as we turn
our attention to the contents of the eternal archetypal space,
in other words its intrinsic structure, we perceive that behind
this formal homogeneity the contents are totally heterogeneous.
If the miracle occurs, and some particular occurrence brings
about a change in our lives so that the doors of our prison are
thrown open as though by an earthquake and our eyes, like
those of Elisha's servant in the story (II Kings 6), 'are opened'
to the space of eternity which encompasses us invisibly on all
sides like the air, then we perceive at once that the space which
we have discovered here is totally different from all the spaces
with which we have previously been concerned. Even when
I first discover one of these other spaces, for example the ego-
space, after it has previously been concealed from me, that
has indeed very far-reaching consequences for my whole
understanding of the world, I am given a new perspective and
reality displays itself to me from a new angle; but nevertheless, this is all nothing more than an extension of my intellectual horizon. It still does not represent a revolution transforming my whole existence. It is quite a different matter
when my eyes are opened to the all-presence of the eternal
world. For what has been disclosed to me then is not merely
a fresh aspect of the enigmatic and inexhaustibly rich reality
in which we live. On the contrary, the transformation which
has thus been brought about involves the whole of reality.
Every field of existence, every aspect which this world
possesses, is suddenly seen in an entirely new light. For the
fundamental characteristic of temporality, which impresses its
special mark upon every sector of reality as a whole, is now

not merely eliminated at one single point; it is overcome all along the line. If there is a suprapolar world, it affords the universe an eternal counterpoise. That must necessarily make itself apparent in all fields simultaneously. It is as when, over a landscape which has been entirely shrouded in darkness, a flash of lightning shines out. An unearthly light is suddenly shed over all the hill-tops, all the valleys, all the ravines, all the heights and all the depths. Similarly, when the wall of the prison of temporality is breached at one point, every field of life, from the greatest to the smallest and from the most intimate and central to the most peripheral, is lighted up by an eternal radiance. Everyone who has found the way from secularism to belief experiences an astonishing transformation of his entire conception of reality. And conversely, for anyone whose faith has broken down under the impact of some severe blow of fate, the whole sky suddenly grows dark above his head and reality appears to him as a landscape which is wrapped in gloom. Both the illumination, which has taken place in the first case, and the darkening, which occurs in the second case, begin at the central point in the picture of reality and immediately spread from there until they cover the whole.

But what is the central point of the overall picture? It is, as we saw in our first chapters, the centre of vision, from which the whole is seen. It is my own ego, which sits, so to speak, as a spectator in the darkened space of non-objectivity while world events pass before it on the stage of objectivity, and which in turn, at the particular position in the world to which it is linked by its destiny, intervenes volitionally and actively in the world process. We have seen, both in the chapter entitled 'The Problem of Space in Modern Physics' and in the chapter on 'The Psychical Content of the World', that, even though one may for theoretical purposes leave it out of account, this centre of vision is still an essential part of the contemporary world-picture. It is only at this all-predominant centre of the overall picture that the light can shine out which illuminates the whole. If there is a path which leads to God, it can be disclosed only from this unobservable central point. This fact is of crucial practical importance. As soon as I disregard my own ego and devote my attention to the objective space for its own sake, God remains entirely invisible. All inferences from the existence of the objective world to the basis of this existence, or from the purpose-serving structure of objective reality to a purpose-giving being which has produced it, lead always, so long as I leave my self out of account, only to some still more remote cosmic cause, which must itself be the effect of some even more remote cause, and so on *ad infinitum*. Or else they lead to a general idea of God, such as might stand behind the whole, in other words to an entirely non-committal marginal concept which cannot be a source of strength to me in my practical life. It is only when my own ego, this invisible centre of vision around which the whole cosmic process revolves, is revealed in a new light, that there can shine out from this central point the lightning flash which 'from the beginning until the going down' pervades everything with its radiance and illumines all the fields of life.

But in what, then, does this light consist, from which these powerful effects proceed? If the omnipresence of God may be spoken of as a space, indeed as the archetypal space, which forms the eternal counterpoise to the totality of all polar spaces, and from which, in consequence, the whole world can be levered out of its position, then this must reveal itself by the fact that, when this archetypal space, too, is disclosed, the same law operates which we have observed in all the other cases when a new space has been discovered. We have seen that when a new space emerges something thereby all at once becomes possible which within the space previously known would have involved a contradiction. The 'Either/Or', the conflict of mutually exclusive alternatives, which had characterized the structure of the previous space, is eliminated. There comes into operation something which within the framework of the space previously known was rendered impossible by the law of the 'excluded third', a *tertium,* a third possibility, overcoming the antithesis between the two alternatives which in the previous space were alone admissible under the rule that 'a third is not given', *tertium non datur.* If in the all-presence of God a new space is disclosed to us, this must reveal itself in the fact that this discovery is accom-

M

panied by an occurrence which resembles, though on an infinitely higher plane, the occurrence which accompanied all the other space-discoveries we have so far considered.

And that is in fact the case. With the presence of God a conflict of alternatives is eliminated, an 'either or' from which we cannot escape so long as this entirely new space is still hidden from us. What is the nature of this 'either or'? The 'either or' within which the polar world holds me captive can become visible to me only when I turn my thoughts to my self. For, as we have already seen, it is only from this central point in the overall picture that the great transformation with which we are here concerned can begin. If this transformation is to take hold of me I must, therefore, 'come to myself'. I must cease to escape from myself, to be oblivious of myself and to abandon myself intoxicatedly to the impressions of the objective world, which storm in upon me from all sides, distract me and divert my attention from myself. I must adopt the attitude which the prodigal son adopted at the moment when, in the words of our Lord's parable, 'he came to himself' (Luke 15.17). I must, as Heidegger describes it in his existential philosophy, have myself called or fetched back from the impersonal 'one', into which I escaped and in which I am now held fast. As soon as I have thus ceased to flee from myself, as soon as I am 'by myself', I become aware that in this instant of the world, just as in every earlier and later instant, I am confronted by two questions which I cannot evade. The first question is this: Where do I come from? How has the purely passive occurrence come about, whereby I have received my self, so that I am he who I am, this one and no other? In this first reception (*Urempfang*), in consequence of which I am, without any possibility of exchange, this ego from which I cannot myself free myself, two factors are, in view of what has previously been said, necessarily involved. Firstly the presence of this particular invariable subject, which is still independent of the corporeality to which I am attached and of the position within the objective world to which I am linked by my destiny, independent, that is to say, of my 'being cast into my *there*'. And the second factor which this first reception involves is the variable side of my

existence, the determining of the *here* and the *now* into
which I am 'cast' by that enigmatic original act (*Urakt*) which
took place entirely without action on my part and which
allows me no means of freeing myself.

The second problem, one which I cannot evade when once
I have 'come to myself', is not a problem of theoretical knowledge but a problem of immediate practical significance. It
results from the fact that the situation into which I have
been 'cast' is part, not of a world at rest, but of a world in
motion, a 'wandering world', a world, that is to say, which is
involved in continual change and which is borne downstream
like a ship on the ever-flowing river of time. From this it
follows that at every moment it must be decided anew what
shape the world is to assume in the ensuing moment. If
therefore, as we have seen, I am 'cast' into this particular
position in the world, I am thereby stationed at a point in the
immensely long front line of the present cosmic instant, and
I am obliged, whether I wish it or not, to participate in the
movement which this front line makes. In other words, I too
must play my own small part in helping to decide how the
world is to look at the next instant. The decision with regard
to this has not yet been taken. It is an obscure future into
which I am advancing. Consequently there is no escaping the
question: What am I to do at this moment? Which direction shall I take? Even if I attempt to remain inactive, to
abstain, as it were, from voting, that is still doing something.
Indeed, the 'non-voters' party' often decides the issue. So I
must do something. I must advance in one direction or another. Which direction shall it be?

The second of these two questions is obviously even more
urgent than the first. For the question of where I come from
may be left unanswered for a time if I adopt the position that
'I come and know not whence, I go and know not whither'.
But even if I have no answer for the question of where I come
from and why I am 'cast' into this particular position in the
world, I must still in any circumstances take action. It is
therefore with this second question that we must begin, the
question concerning the direction of my activity. As soon as
I am entirely alone by myself with this question, beset on all

sides by the concrete situation of this fateful hour—let us think, for example, of the choice of a profession, which determines the whole course of my life, or the choice of a wife, or the vitally important instructions which a doctor has to give every day during his consultations—then quite involuntarily, perhaps helplessly and desperately, I look out for something which will ease the torment of making a choice and relieve me of the burden of coming to a decision, some motive or indication which will show me the direction I should take.   I have need of something that will free me from the paralysing sense of arbitrariness and indecision with which for the moment, like Hercules at the cross-roads, I stand face to face with the multitude of possibilities available to me.   What I require is a necessity upon which I can base my action, a sanction or authority or warrant.   Only if that is accorded to me can I view with equanimity the decision I am taking. When I look out for something which will give me the support I need in taking my decision, I become quite clearly aware that within the space of the polar world, in which for the time being I am confined, only two ways are open to me in this quest.   The first way is to have recourse to some value or other which is fairly generally recognized in the world and to endeavour to steer my course into the obscurity of the future by the aid of this value.   I set out, for example, from a reality, which, as almost everybody is agreed, must be maintained and promoted.   It may be my family, or my nation and its culture, or a political constitution, a social order or an economic system which appears to guarantee the liberty and the well-being of mankind.   And then I relate to this value the concrete situation in which I am now obliged to take action.   I ask myself what my decision must be in this my present situation if this value is to be respected.

Even without thoroughly exploring all the possible results of this course in the light of the history of ethics, the history of legal institutions and the history of political and social structures, it is very easy to demonstrate that, so long as my outlook is restricted to the space of this polar world, any reality of this kind by which I may seek to orientate myself, even such a comprehensive and universally acknowledged reality as the nation, the race or humanity, is 'temporal', that is to say it is involved in this world's process of becoming and decaying. Indeed, the whole of humanity, or even the whole surface of the earth upon which the nations have built up their cultures, could be transformed within a few hours by atomic energy into dust and smoke. A reality which is so transitory can, therefore, in no case, by the mere fact of its existence, impose upon me the duty of sacrificing my life in order to preserve and advance it. For this reality exists only for a limited time. There was a time when it did not yet exist, and there will come a time when it will no longer exist, a time, that is to say, when the claim which this value-quantity makes upon me, with its demand that I should devote myself to its service, will quite automatically have lapsed. But if this claim is at some point in time certain to lapse, then the force with which this reality binds me to its service possesses even now only a *relative* character. The power to command allegiance which is possessed by a value-quantity that is restricted within temporal bounds and has become historical, the sanction it affords me if I endeavour to uphold and promote it, always rests only on some more comprehensive decision which has been taken earlier and of which my personal decision at this moment becomes a part. This higher decision may have been taken by an individual who sets a precedent and stands before my eyes as a model and an ideal. Or else it may be a collective decision, which has been taken by a supra-individual body, such as the organic unity of an entire people, a state or a Church, and has crystallized in an established ethic, a customary, ancestral way of life, the code of honour of a class, or a political order and legislative system. We do not intend, in the present context, to examine in detail the various patterns of individual and communal life which have arisen in this way, for we are concerned in this connexion only with the underlying feature which is common to all these forms. Behind all codes of ethics, all ideals of life, all moral standards, constitutions and judicial systems, there are always decisions which have been taken already in earlier times, either collective decisions or else the decisions of leading individual personalities. If we consider closely any one of these earlier decisions which might indicate the direction we should take in the critical situation of the present, it is at once apparent that this decision, too, was taken by human beings, that is to say by beings resembling ourselves. These beings may have stood on a relatively higher plane than ourselves; but in the respect which concerns us here they were in the same situation as we are. For them, too, the decision was not unequivocally indicated in advance either by the situation or by an infallible voice of conscience or by a known reality. They had to decide for themselves. Just like us, they had either to carry out their decision with a sense of arbitrariness or else to find first of all some support in a higher decision, one which had already been taken and which provided them with a foundation upon which they could continue to build. And the same is of course true, in its turn, of the higher authority upon which they based themselves. Whether it was a group or an individual personality, it still necessarily depended on some earlier decision which had already been taken, and so on *ad infinitum*.

It is therefore apparent that even in this highest and most central domain of our existence, that in which our moral obligation is anchored, together with everything which gives our life its meaning, we are subject to the same fundamental law of *polarity* as in the elementary relations of the time series and the spatial line. Here, too, nothing exists which might be capable of supporting and sustaining itself. There is nowhere anything self-sufficient and self-contained. Everywhere we are led to a series which we must follow backwards interminably, on and on, without ever reaching a point at which we may halt. It is the same thing with the moral decisions which we have to take within the polar living-space, as any one of us will at once feel, without much reflection, whenever the decision he is called upon to make requires that he shall be ready to die for a cause in a forlorn hope. If in this situation, in order to summon up courage for the difficult step which I have to take in this matter, I base myself upon the more comprehensive decision which more eminent people than myself have taken before me in similar situations, I see that the ground upon which I would here like to tread is not solid and is not capable of supporting me at this critical juncture. I remain a prisoner of *relativism*. And relativism is not a rock upon which I can stand firmly but sand which gives way if I try to rest the whole weight of my body upon it. It does not possess the power to keep me above water in hours of temptation, when I am in danger of becoming cowardly or of losing my integrity.

When we have been through this experience with relativism, when we have seen for ourselves that it is true to say that 'whoever eats relativism dies of it' and that the underlying attitude of relativism paralyses our will and renders impossible any decision to sacrifice our entire existence, then we are involuntarily impelled to break free from this condition. At first sight this seems to be impossible. For relativism is like a journey on a railway with no terminus, so that we must travel on from station to station without ever reaching a goal at which we can halt. And yet we may still make an attempt to extricate ourselves by our own efforts from this intolerable situation. How is that possible? The possibility is offered to us in the fact that we can never think out an infinite series to the end; so that, if we move forwards or backwards, we must always make at least a temporary halt at some point or other. We must then, figuratively speaking, drive in a nail at some point, in order to hang everything upon it. If, for example, we wish to define any particular point of time, we must establish a starting point as the basis for our calculation. We may think, for instance, of the ancient Roman chronology, dating *ab urbe condita,* or of the chronology of the Christian era. If we wish to define any physical magnitude, we require a scale by which we can measure but which cannot itself be measured. If we wish to explain the present state of the world, we must go back to some 'primordial state' beyond which we can go no further, for instance the 'original nebular mass'. And so it is in all fields. Once we have perceived that it is necessary to assume something given whenever we wish to measure, to calculate, to think or to act, it follows that we must make up our minds to posit this initial assumption quite consciously, as an autonomous decision, which we human beings carry through with the clear conviction that we are our own masters —*sic volo, sic jubeo,* this is my will and this is my command.

This resolution to bring to a halt by a consciously arbitrary act of violence the unceasing movement in which relativism involves us makes what is no doubt its first appearance in the history of western thought when, in the time of the Greek Sophists, Protagoras pronounces his dictum that 'Man is the measure of all things'. Since this attitude always starts out from an assumption, i.e. from something posited, we will call it positivism. But we are not taking this word here in the general sense in which it was later used by Auguste Comte and in which it has subsequently been employed over and over again. According to this modern conception positivism is any understanding of the world which excludes all metaphysical cosmic substrata and which recognizes as reality only what is immediately perceptible to our senses. In this book we are looking back behind August Comte, back to Protagoras, and we understand by positivism the conviction that everywhere, in the physical sphere as well as in the sphere of law and morality, we must ourselves establish the scale by which we measure, and ourselves determine the point of departure from which we set out.

Positivism has brought about a catastrophic lowering of spiritual standards. It presents a grave danger for the whole culture of the West. It is undermining all the foundations of the law, the state, morality and religion.[1] So long as positivism is in the saddle, there is nothing which is certain in itself, independently of decisions of the human will. That which has been made effective only by men can also be made ineffective by men. That which is merely the product of a particular situation may be annulled when the wind changes and a revolution supervenes. A value which is only posited by men has no right to demand that I should sacrifice my existence to it. And a value which owes its validity solely to a human decision is never worthy of absolute reliance. For if I put my trust in this value, I must myself summon up the courage which this act of trust requires. That demands a great effort. For the question repeatedly arises: Whence does

---

[1] cf. *Die Geschichte der Rechtswissenschaft im Spiegel der Metaphysik* (*The History of Jurisprudence as reflected by Metaphysics*), by Walter Schönfeld, Stuttgart and Berlin, 1943, p. 16ff.

this value derive its sanction? I must suppress this question by force; I must forbid myself and everyone else to enquire into the antecedents of this value-quantity. I must repress the questions which inevitably keep arising in this connexion. From this there ultimately arises an attitude of convulsion, a fanaticism which is the sign of an inner uncertainty. In difficult situations, when my existence is at its lowest ebb, when I am inwardly down and out, this value of my own determining will give me no support. My confidence in the reality behind it is never more than an *attitude* which I must produce in myself; it is not that effortless reception of a gift, which alone is capable of giving me inner stability when my own strength is exhausted.

A particularly graphic example of the nature and the effects of positivism was that system of which, in the most recent period of German history, we have witnessed the rise and the collapse. The system rested upon two *postulates*. The first of these was provided when Rosenberg, in the *Myth of the Twentieth Century,* set up the 'racial soul' as the 'supreme value', about whose antecedents, as he expressly states, no further questions were to be asked. The second postulate consisted in the 'will of the Leader (*Führer*)' being declared to be the ultimate 'source of law' and the supreme authority for all legal decisions throughout the administration of justice, above which there was no higher authority to which an appeal might be addressed. There is no need today to waste words in telling of the practical consequences of the two *posita* upon which this positivist state was constructed.

We can see what disastrous effects both *relativism* and *positivism* entail, not only for the political life of the community and for the administration of justice, but also for our lives as individual persons. How can the power of these two schools of thought be broken? It is of no value to protest against them with moral indignation and to cry out for measures of defence against this national peril. Such countermeasures can serve no useful purpose in combating these forces. For both relativism and positivism are a necessity so long as the law of polarity remains effective and unbroken. And the law of polarity is quite as inescapable as the three-dimensional space, within which we are all confined with our perceptions and our conceptions, whether we turn our eyes towards our immediate environment, for example the neighbouring house which we can see through our window, or whether we gaze out with the giant telescope into the immeasurable distances of the cosmic nebulae. We can nowhere break free from the endless prison of three-dimensional space. The geometrical structure of the Euclidian space determines the form even of the figments of our imagination and our dreams. And just as inescapably as our perceptions are confined within the three-dimensional space, so too the totality of all the relations in which we move is confined within the fundamental form of polarity. The fact of our being situated in the polar world-form is independent of any volitional decision of our own. We find ourselves there even before we being to will and to think. It is simply our destiny.

16. THE SYNTHESIS OF RELATIVISM AND POSITIVISM

We have seen that, so long as we remain in the polar space, we are enclosed between the only two possibilities which it leaves open to us, as though between the two walls of a defile. There is no way out from this dilemma. All values, all attempts to establish a scale of values and to arrange values in order of precedence, are subject to this 'either or', the inescapable choice between these two alternatives. Either they are the products of a historical development, which, in the course of time and under a multiplicity of national and cultural influences, has led to these values; in which case they are relative magnitudes, magnitudes which have come into being and which can cease to be. Or else they have been established by sovereign decisions of human legislators, rulers or founders of states; in which case they are things posited, *posita*.

Is there any means of escape from this 'either or', this painful choice between relativism and positivism? That is possible only on one condition, namely that there must be disclosed to me an entirely new space, with a structure wholly different from that of the space of polarity in all its forms. This must reveal itself by the fact that, by virtue of this new space which is here discovered, all at once something is possible which within the polar space would be a contradiction. In this higher space, over which we cannot ourselves dispose, the 'either or' of the polar space must be eliminated and the gulf must be bridged which in the polar space separates the two possibilities, relativism and positivism. Effect must be given to the proposition *tertium datur,* a third is given. That 'third' must come into play which was 'excluded' by the structure of the polar space. How can this come about? Only by the emergence of a synthesis in which both goals are achieved, the goals towards which both relativism and positivism have been striving in vain. In the previous chapter we gained a clear view of the nature of relativism and positivism from the effects these two attitudes of mind produce at the central point which constitutes the focus of the overall picture of reality. This central point is my own ego, intervening in the course of events as a responsible agent at this crucial cosmic instant. It is at this central point that we must realize what it signifies when the suprapolar space is disclosed. Only when the light shines out at this point can the overall picture of reality be suffused with the radiance of this light. Once the structure of the suprapolar space has become clear to us at this central point, we shall also be able to recognize the principle of this structure, as will later become evident, in all the other domains of reality.

The synthesis between relativism and positivism which takes effect in the suprapolar space becomes apparent to us if we perceive clearly what is the goal at which both relativism and positivism are aiming. The relativist does not wish to bind himself to a particular value offered him by reality. He wishes to base his life upon reality as a whole. The world in which we live does, indeed, confront us with an immense variety of different possible ways of life, ethical principles and mental attitudes. If I am relativistically inclined I select one possibility at random from amongst the immense wealth of possibilities which are here available to me. I must, after all, move in some direction or other, and set out along some path or other. But in doing this I am always conscious of the fact that I might just as well be moving in the opposite direction, and I am unwilling to bind myself for ever to any one particular way of life. I would like to retain my capacity for sharing sympathetically in the acceptance of absolutely all possible values, points of view and mental attitudes, on the principle that ' *tout comprendre c'est tout pardonner* '. This sympathetic broadmindedness and understanding tolerance has at all times been the special charm of relativism. That is why it has always attracted the aestheticians. But this universalistic, all-comprehending broadmindedness robs the relativist of his inner stability and leaves him without a coherent moral standpoint. His awareness of the fact that, unlike Luther, ' here I stand, I can do *any* other' renders him incapable of manly action and of whole-hearted devotion to a cause.

This brings us to the second possibility which is available within the polar space, namely to positivism. I need something to which I can devote my life unconditionally and unrestrictedly. But within the polar world there is nothing unconditional; there are only entities which are conditional upon one another and which stand in a relative dependence upon one another. In these circumstances only one course is open to me whereby I can free myself by my own efforts from the paralysing sense of the arbitrariness of my activity. I bind myself to one possibility and strive valiantly to smother and repress all doubts and questions regarding the exclusive legitimacy of this particular way of life. In this way I acquire a coherent point of view, but only by paying the high price of a fanatical narrowmindedness and an attitude of convulsion, forbidding myself and others to enquire into the antecedents of the supreme value to which I have sworn allegiance.

Is there any means of escape from this dilemma between relativism and positivism? Is there a 'third' which will raise us above the 'Either/Or', the bare alternative between these two? This is possible only by virtue of the suprapolar space. By means of the suprapolar space the abyss is bridged which separates the two possibilities which were alone available to us in the polar space, and the conflict between them is resolved in a higher unity. In what does this synthesis of relativism and positivism consist, which the suprapolar space renders possible? All those men whose actions have been

directed by an 'inner task' or mission acted in the certainty
that 'what we are fighting for is the achievement of the purpose of the *whole* world of creation'. St. John the Evangelist,
one of the first eye-witnesses of the life of Jesus and hearers
of His word, sums up his impression of Christ when he says,
at the beginning of his first Epistle: 'We have seen and bear
witness and show unto you *the* life', and again, in the introduction to his Gospel: 'In him was *the* life . . . all things
were made by it, and without it was not any thing made that
was made.' In other words, the womb from which at the very
beginning of creation the whole universe came forth is the
Logos which in Christ became flesh. There is a similar passage in the Epistle to the Hebrews: 'He upholdeth all things
(i.e. the universe) by the word of his power.' And again, Paul
says of Christ: 'All things were created by him, and for him:
and he is before all things, and by him all things consist [i.e.
all things are summed up in Him]. . . . He is the fulness of
him that fulfilleth all things in all things' (Col. 1). All these
tremendous, universal pronouncements rest upon the certainty
that He who has come among us in the name of God speaks
in terms of the meaning of the cosmic whole. He sees into
the depths of the cosmos. When in the time of the first world
war the poet, Max Dauthendey, in the midst of overwhelming
vicissitudes had discovered Christ, he summed up the impression which Christ's words made upon him as he read the
New Testament in the sentence: 'Each of His words is spoken
out of the centre of the universe.' Here then for a start the
aim of relativism is achieved, that all-embracing breadth
which comprises the whole wealth of the immense plenitude
of reality. But if there is a suprapolar space, then this breadth
of horizon does not have to be paid for, as was the case with
relativism, by a corresponding loss of that unity and coherence
in the directing of my life which alone enables me to devote
it unreservedly to a great cause. For the Creator's sanction
invests this cosmic hour and this cosmic situation with a quite
concrete purpose. The accent of eternity rests upon one quite
definite point where there is revealed to me the direction in
which now, in the name of God, I must go forward. In the
lens of the burning-glass the whole wealth of the sun's rays is

concentrated at a single point. This produces such a heat that dry grass catches fire if the glass is focused upon it. So, too, the whole abundance of power, of which 'in the beginning' the universe was born, is concentrated at the one point where he whom God has sent speaks and acts. It is the consciousness of acting in accordance with the meaning and spirit of the universe that sets the messenger of God aflame and fills him with the certainty that he bears the message which is addressed to all. The precepts which he gives, and which he derives from his unrestricted view of the world, are, as Ralph Waldo Trine says, 'in harmony with the infinite'. And consequently they achieve what relativism sought to gain by following the mistaken path of tolerance. The messenger of God, from his understanding of the meaning of the whole, issues the concrete marching-order for this hour, which overcomes all hesitations and renders us capable of steering a course between the rocks that threaten on either hand. That which was from the beginning ($\dot{a}\pi$' $\dot{a}\rho\chi\hat{\eta}\varsigma$), and in which was potentially contained the whole intrinsic meaning of the world that was still to come into being, is here revealed in an individual figure, in which the whole abundance of light of the cosmos is concentrated as though in a focus. And so Christ does not come into the world as a stranger; 'He came unto his own', as one who was at home in the universe, as the Son in the house which His Father has built. He is therefore in a position to give commands which are in accord with the purpose of the whole creation. Christ's commandments therefore, for anyone who is of this world, are not the decrees of a foreign usurper who has arrogated to himself an unjust authority over us. His voice is the voice of the shepherd whose sheep are his own. Christ can say to the pagan Pilate: 'Every one that is of the truth (i.e. anyone who is honest with himself) heareth my voice.'

Unlike all human ethical doctrines, which are historically, nationally and culturally conditioned and possess only limited validity, Christ, according to the conviction of the primitive church, is the Kyrios, the only one entitled to this name which is above all names, the supreme authority, above which there is no higher power and by which the final decision is taken with regard to every value that comes within our field of vision —the supreme yardstick by which all things are measured. This authority is like the lighthouse by which ships may steer their course when they have to pass by night through a dangerous channel which is full of rocks. If such a paramount authority is found to exist, then the aim of positivism, too, is achieved, for positivism seeks a supreme value, the antecedents of which do not require investigation.

And so a synthesis is achieved between the goals of relativism and of positivism. Only when this synthesis exists is the question settled regarding the origin of the sanction for our action. Only then can we joyfully face death for the cause in which we are fighting. But we cannot ourselves find this synthesis which invests our activity with a holy necessity. That is impossible already for the reason that we, with our limited horizon, are unable to survey the whole abundance and depth of the universe. We cannot, therefore, deduce what is the 'order of the hour' from our experience and observation of the reality around us, for, indeed, we can descry only an infinitesimally minute fraction of reality as a whole. The 'central vision', as Jakob Boehme called it, that insight which penetrates the whole, must come to us as a gift. We can receive it only by 'revelation'. Nothing of our own devising can free us from the sense of the arbitrariness of our decision. That is why we cannot prove and demonstrate with cogent arguments that this highest commanding authority is given to us in Christ, the Fulfiller and Perfecter of the law of the Old Testament and of all other earlier ethical doctrines. In order to prove that Christ possesses this authority, we should need, indeed, to assess His commandments by some higher criterion. But if any such criterion were found, then Christ would no longer be the Kyrios, the supreme authority. There is, therefore, only one basis upon which we can become certain of the authority of Christ. It is that which, according to St. John's Gospel, our Lord himself affords us when he says: 'My doctrine is not mine, but his that sent me. If any man will do his will, he shall know of the doctrine, whether it be of God, or whether I speak of myself' (John 7.16f.). In the attitude of a spectator, then, this certainty cannot be achieved. But as soon as we venture, on the strength of His words, to follow His commandments in simple active obedience, we experience the 'knowledge' ($\gamma\iota\gamma\nu\acute{\omega}\sigma\kappa\epsilon\iota\nu$) of which Jesus speaks in this passage. We realize that the ground upon which we are now treading will bear our weight. We see that we are acting here in accordance with the intention and the spirit of the Power that has created the universe. We feel beneath our feet the rock of eternity, which is sufficient in itself and which sustains us through all the hardships of life without our having to make the least effort to hold fast to it.

From the standpoint of the polar space this experience is totally incomprehensible. For it is the reverse of the convulsive effort by which positivism is constrained to posit its supreme value and to hold fast to it. It is comprehensible only if there is a suprapolar space within which reality as a whole, which in the polar space resolves itself into a number of interminable series, is viewed synoptically in a higher order as a unity. The impression which the personality of Christ makes upon us discloses to us that eternal archetypal space in which we are situated together with the whole of reality but to which we were blind so long as we were held captive by the polar world. Jesus says, after the healing of the man who was born blind, 'I am come into this world, that they which see not might see' (John 9.39). In other words, He compares the change which we undergo when we become subject to His power with the transformation of the whole conception of reality which one who was born blind, and who has previously known only sensations of sound and touch, experiences when suddenly the whole wealth of the three-dimensional solid space is disclosed to him. On our entrance into the discipleship of Christ we see the whole of reality with new eyes. We are admitted into a higher order and able to receive what this higher order affords us. We are like a radio antenna that is attuned to the invisible waves which pass through the entire universe. This is not the place to expound more fully the witness of Christ in the New Testament. We may refer back for this purpose to the second volume of the present work. In the present context all that concerned us was to understand, so far as that is at all possible, the peculiar relation in which the suprapolar space stands with respect to this entire world of polar affinities that encompasses us on all sides.

The characteristic feature of all those who stand within the field of force of Jesus is that attitude which is equally far removed from relativism and from positivism. The deep repose of eternity which underlies their speech and their actions is fundamentally different from the restlessness in which the relativist lives, cast hither and thither, as he is, between opposite attitudes and ways of life, and also from the convulsive fanaticism of the positivist, who is obliged to cling by his own efforts to the foundation upon which he stands. The deep repose which this third basic attitude affords to mankind rests upon the certainty of acting in accordance with the ultimate meaning of the universe in its bearing on this instant, in accordance, that is to say, with what must eventually be found, before the conscience of all mankind, to be right. Paul speaks of the 'holy compulsion' which controls his actions in the words 'Necessity is laid upon me ($\dot{a}\nu\acute{a}\gamma\kappa\eta$ $\gamma\acute{a}\rho$ $\mu o\iota$ $\acute{e}\pi\acute{\iota}\kappa\epsilon\iota\tau a\iota$)' (I Cor. 9.16). He knows that even though all men reject the way he is going, it is the way ordained by the Power which has created and will perfect the whole world. What he is doing is in harmony with the origin and purpose of the universe.

We do not ourselves need to assign the task which rests upon this eternal foundation. We receive it from the hand of a higher Power. It comes to us as a gift. And consequently we may rest effortlessly within it. In the eternal Will which here commands us we are secure. This Will is entirely independent of our own will and of our own decision. When we obey it, that is not a case of being willing but of being compelled or, better, of being permitted. The question regarding the origin of the authority for our action, a question which in the space of polarity had always led us either to relativism or to positivism, is here resolved in the eternal sanction which is granted to us as a gift. For now we no longer require any power in order to hold fast to this mission and to prove its authority, for this mission is secure in its own strength. We may devote all our energy to its execution. The certainty

N

that 'God wills it', the fact that our will is at rest in the eternal Will, imparts to us an invincible strength in the face of all attempts to divert us from our path by means of enticements or threats. It invests us with a mysterious authority over men, even when we are quite alone, face to face with a superior majority. We need only think of the words which Luther spoke at the Diet of Worms when he was in danger of being burnt at the stake: 'Here I stand. I can do no other.' Or the words of the apostles before the Sanhedrin, which wished to forbid them to proclaim the name of Jesus: 'Whether it be right in the sight of God to hearken unto you more than unto God, judge ye' (Acts 4.19). How is it possible that the action of a weak human being can rest upon so unshakable a foundation? So long as our thinking is solely in terms of the two alternatives which are open to us in the space of polarity, we can never do more than explain to ourselves the fortitude with which the martyrs went to their deaths for their cause as an excess of fanaticism, whereby, even in the face of death, these men clung to the *idée fixe* which had taken possession of them like some mad delusion. But the calmness with which these men came before their judges, the steadfastness with which, in the ages of martyrdom, even children went joyfully to their deaths, cannot be explained as mere auto-suggestive enthusiasm. It cannot be ascribed to any psychological propensity at all which one possesses and another lacks, such as will-power or heroism. It is intelligible only if an omnipresent space exists, which encompasses us all, no matter whether we be children or adults, average people or heroes, and by virtue of which there is a third possible way of existence, one that raises us infinitely far above the two possibilities, relativism and positivism, which lie open to us within the polar space. This third possibility is to rest upon an eternal mission which is in harmony with the meaning of the universe. This mission, which comes to us from the archetypal space of eternity, has such a power to sustain that not the slightest effort is needed in order to hold fast to it. Even the weakest of human beings, one who is by nature frightened of suffering and noticeably timid, is able, if he is sustained by this eternal mission, to defy the whole world and to go to his death with equanimity.

In the times of the persecution of the Christians this has repeatedly been observed with astonishment.

To conclude this chapter we must deal with a misunderstanding which might arise from what has so far been said. What we have been saying might possibly lead us to the idea that the fact of there being a space of eternity is adequately proved when this consciousness of a vocation, which certain historical personages have possessed, somewhere comes before us as a matter of historical certainty, so that historical sources enable us to enter into the attitude of mind out of which this consciousness of a vocation arises. Let us consider, for example, the state of mind in which Amos wrote the words: 'The lion hath roared, who will not fear? Yahweh hath spoken, who can but prophesy?' Or Paul's consciousness of his vocation, when he wrote to the Galatians: 'Paul, an apostle, not of men, neither by a man, but by Jesus Christ and God the Father'; or when, in his epistle to the Corinthians, he said: 'For though I preach the gospel, I have nothing to glory of; . . . woe is unto me, if I preach not the gospel! For if I do this thing willingly, I have a reward: but if against my will, a dispensation of the gospel is committed unto me' (I Cor. 9.16f.). But if we suppose that the space of eternity is disclosed to us whenever we allow ourselves to be impressed by such historical testimonies, that is a grave misunderstanding. For the spell of the polar space, by which we are held captive with all our perceptions, all our imagining and all our thinking, as though in an endless prison, cannot be broken by any causal inference. So long as we are subject to the rule of polar thought, we shall necessarily fit every event, no matter how impressive or extraordinary it may be, into the polar world-picture. Consequently, any causal inference, too, which we may draw from some event of this kind, can always lead us only to relative magnitudes and limited energy-factors which form part of the causal nexus of the polar world. Even the authority of a prophet, who speaks to fulfil the highest mission, can then never be explained except psychologically or pathologically, as proceeding from an *idée fixe*, by which he is obsessed, or from a subconscious complex, which directs his speech and actions like a hidden wire-puller.

We can be released from the bondage of polar thinking, which determines our whole interpretation of the world and all our logical processes, only if, in a totally inexplicable manner, resembling what happens when one who has been born blind receives the gift of sight, there is disclosed to us the new suprapolar space, so that at a single stroke the whole of reality shines out in a new light. If the suprapolar space is disclosed to us at all, it must come into force at once all along the line. Consequently, the new light must necessarily shine out at the central focus in the overall picture of reality, and from there irradiate the whole. This central point in the general picture is precisely what natural science, in accordance with its special task, must deliberately disregard, namely my own ego in its attachment to a particular position in the world of experience. The vocation of which we have spoken, the 'sacred necessity' to which Paul ascribes his mission, the inner task which renders irrelevant any decision of our own, the 'inspiration' which even puts into the mouth of him who is sent by God particular words which he must utter, all this can afford access to the space of eternity, not if it merely confronts me as an objective factor in the lives of other people, but only if, at this moment, I am myself drawn in into this process, and if, in consequence of this, there rests upon some quite definite way of life which I must in this hour make my own, and upon some task which this very day sets before me, the accent of eternity. The eternal mission which here takes control of me will, of course, in most cases not be a special mission which I alone have to fulfil; it will be a collective vocation to which thousands, perhaps millions, of others will at the same time be subject, for instance the general mission, which has in all centuries been incumbent upon the Church of Christ, of being the 'salt of the earth' and the 'light of the world', and, in the struggle against the powers of hatred and vengeance, of initiating a 'revolution of love'. Even with these collective vocations and general tasks the point at which the hidden space of the eternal world emerges, and at which everything shines out in a new light, is always solely at the place at which I myself, as the invisible centre of co-ordinates in the picture of reality, am caught up and carried along by the great stream of this collective movement. So long as this point is lacking, the heaven is hidden and the world is dark, even though I may have busied myself for years with a detailed study of the sources relating to that interesting problem in the history of religion, the vocation and inspiration of the prophets. I can then always understand this problem only in purely secularistic terms, regarding it, for example, as an irruption from the individual or collective subconscious.

17. THE SUPRAPOLAR ORIGIN OF OUR PERSONAL EXISTENCE

In order to illustrate the change which this brings about, I have begun by considering one of the two questions which confront me when I have stopped running away from myself and have 'come to myself', the immediately urgent question of what, in this critical moment, I am to do. We must now, with the same purpose in mind, turn to the second question, a question which I cannot evade if I have given up my attempt to escape from myself. This is the question of where I come from. Why am I this ego and not another? Why do I stand at this point within the world, and not at some other point at which, after all, I might really just as well stand? Once this question is raised I am confronted with the ultimate riddle of my personal existence. If I seek for a solution to this puzzle I am caught, as I was with the question regarding the authority for my actions, in a narrow defile, as it were, between the two cliffs of the 'Either/Or', the clear-cut alternative between relativism and positivism, and for the time being I can see no way out. For, indeed, the space of the encounter between the I and the Thou consists of an immense multitude of millions and thousands of millions of subjects, all of them solitary ego-monads, each possessing immediate knowledge only of itself and separated from all the others as though by an ocean. Why, amidst these thousands of millions of 'souls', must I always be only this one particular soul? Why can I not be rid of myself? Why must I drag around with me for all time the burden of the past of this one person? Why can I not exchange with another person? And why am I always fettered, at least for this earthly life, to this particular position in space and time?

For this pressing question 'Why?', in which the whole destiny of my life is implied, relativism has simply no answer. For no reason can be perceived why I am precisely this man and stand here at precisely this spot. We have already seen that neither of the two necessities which are possible within the polar space, neither logical necessity nor causal necessity, is applicable to the state of affairs with which we are here concerned. I might really just as well be any other one of the millions of subjects which fill the I-Thou space. I might just as well have been 'cast' into the position in which you are standing, or in which anyone else is standing who was born at another time and belongs to another nation and another country. It is then a matter of complete indifference that I am precisely this man and not simply anyone else. No reason can be perceived for my being attached for the duration of my life to precisely this point in the cosmic space. In fact it ought to be extremely easy to alter my position and to exchange the rôle I have to play for the rôle played by absolutely anyone else. But actually, of course, it is quite impossible for me to change places with someone who is better off than I am. We are certainly not granted a 'metempsychosis', at least during our lifetime. My being bound to this position, as Prometheus was bound to the rock, without any apparent reason, is, then, a totally meaningless and ridiculous *chance*. I cannot even call it *destiny*. This sublime word is quite inappropriate here, for there is no authority by which this destiny could have been 'destined' to me. I can only say that it is like a game of hazard in which the pure chance of the throw of the dice decides whether I am to lose all or to win a fortune.

If that is the position, then it is quite impossible for me to take seriously the fact that, of all the thousands of millions of human destinies which are being worked out on the earth, I am obliged to assume and to play out to the bitter end the rôle of this particular human being. All I can do is to adopt the attitude we adopt when somebody has played a silly joke on us. I can only put a good face on it, and accept, with annoyance or with a sense of humour as the case may be, the rôle which through no action on my part has fallen to my lot. A man who does not take his personal existence seriously, and who regards himself only as a specimen of a type, interchangeable with any other specimen of the same type, this is the typical 'man of the masses' (*Massenmensch*). He says to himself: 'I am no more than a wave in an irresistibly advancing stream. As an individual I am nothing. I can only merge in the mass. As an individual I have no responsibility. I lay the whole burden of responsibility on the supra-individual mass organizations which alone are capable of making history. I conform with what *one* does, what *one* thinks, what *one* wears and what *one* reads. Only the mass can decide.' This indifference towards one's own personal existence is shown in practice by suicide being taken quite lightly. If I no longer get any fun out of my personal lot, I can at any time throw it away. *Patet exitus.* Death is open to me. This Asiatic indifference to our personal existence is the only possibility at our disposal so long as the Thou relation is considered only within the framework of the polar world-space. That is *relativism*.

The other alternative is *positivism,* the belief that I have the divine authority to fix my own position. In fact, of course, positivism in this sense is nowadays hardly maintained seriously, for it is opposed to the general trend of the times. But during that great period of German history, the Napoleonic wars, it played a decisive part in the history of ideas. It is the very opposite extreme from the Asiatic deification of the mass. It is that Titanic idea of Fichte's, that by virtue of my one-ness with the absolute ego I at every moment determine my position anew. My existence is a positive activity, whereby at every instant in time I re-create myself in absolute freedom. By virtue of this self-determination I stand face to face with the whole objective world in sovereign independence. To the objective world-forces which confront me I can cry: 'I am eternal and I defy your might. Fall upon me, all of you . . . all you elements . . . my will alone . . . shall soar boldly and coldly above the wreckage of the universe.' This was an idea of unheard-of boldness and overwhelming power, and it inspired the youth of Prussia, as they went into the Wars of Liberation, with an unparalleled self-assurance even in the face of death. No one has ventured until now to apply the term positivism to this outlook, which endowed the young warriors in those campaigns with the power to risk their lives, for the word is generally used in the sense in which Auguste Comte used it and which we have already described. And yet this inner attitude bears all the essential marks of positivism! One may even say that positivism has here attained its culmination and has penetrated into the innermost domain of life. An individual ego here makes a violent and gigantic effort to break out from the prison of his individual existence, this existence which compels him always merely to be either this man or one of the thousands of millions who confront him as the ever-alien others. This ego wishes to be the all-embracing ego, which bears within it all the other egos as its own individualizations, and therefore takes up its own position in proud solitude.

Here too, as we have seen was the case with all the other forms of positivism, it is only by dint of a supreme effort that it is possible to carry out this attempt to raise one link in the interminable series to the status of an ultimate *positum* the antecedents of which are not open to enquiry. It has been said with truth that the faith in the ego, which speculative idealism proclaimed, can be maintained only in a state of extreme enthusiasm, a state of continual intoxicated self-exaltation, that impassioned glorification of the self to which the whole style of Fichte's speeches and writings owes its compelling power. As soon as this elation has died down and the youthful exuberance has given place to a sober consideration of the facts, we come to the depressing realization that unfortunately it is not actually the case that by a sovereign act of liberation I have determined my own situation. Otherwise it would necessarily be in my power to revoke this determination and to extinguish myself again. And yet, at every attempt at suicide, whereby I endeavour to free myself from a desperate predicament, I find that, even though I can destroy my body, I can never do more than hope that this brings with it the extinction of my ego, for the extinction of my ego is something which I cannot directly bring about. I am not master of my consciousness. I cannot even erase from the tables of my memory a single tormenting recollection which pursues me; still less, then, can I annihilate my consciousness in its entirety.

We have now formed a clear picture of the two ways which alone stand open to me within the polar space when I am beset by the question of the ultimate basis of my personal existence. Here, too, the disclosure of the suprapolar space brings about the same transformation of the whole situation as it did in connexion with the question: 'What am I to do now?' Here, too, there comes into view a quite unexpected third possibility, which points to a way of escape from the dilemma within which I am confined. In what does this third possibility consist? When dealing with our first question, the question of what I am to do, we found ourselves confronted, as soon as the suprapolar space was disclosed to us, with an incomprehensible gift. This gift is a basis for living, to which I no longer myself need to cling convulsively, but which supports and sustains me, and upon which I can rest effortlessly. Resting upon this foundation I can defy the whole world. It is a foundation which gives me the power to give to others, too, the support which they need, on the principle that *teneo quia teneor*: I hold because I am held. It is only now, when I know of the gift that is implied in the words 'mission', 'vocation' and 'task', that I am vouchsafed an answer to the other question, the question of whence I receive these things, and of the kind of ultimate authority that sets this task. This commanding authority, as well as the command itself which emanates from it, can become visible only when I have 'come to myself' and when I am quite alone with myself as the non-intuitional ego, distinguishing itself from the entire objective world which confronts it. So long as I am still a fugitive from myself, oblivious of myself, and intoxicated and carried away by the whirlpool of the objective world-process, I am not amenable to any task which can finally set me free both from relativistic indecision and from the strenuous endeavour to set myself a task of my own. For the objective world, which is trying to draw me into its domain, does indeed contain on its own account, in every situation, an infinite number of possibilities in favour of which I might decide. Within the objective world an infinite number of ways lie open on all sides, leading into the obscurity of the future. Consequently, the task, by virtue of which the accent of eternity falls on one of these many possible ways, cannot emanate from the objective world itself. It cannot result of its own accord from the objectively given situation of the present moment, nor can it be deduced from the circumstances. It can come only from a space which has a structure contrary to that of the intuitional world but which nevertheless comprises within itself the whole of reality. From this there follows, at the very outset, an important consequence with regard to the nature of the authority from which this task comes to us. The commanding authority, with which I have to deal here, cannot be anything which is designated by a neuter noun, such as 'life' or 'destiny' or 'fate', which casts me on to the shores of this world just as the breakers cast a shell-fish on to the shore of the sea. For a neuter noun is always used in speaking of an impersonal thing which confronts us objectively. If the authority which sets me my task cannot be represented by a neuter noun, if it cannot be anything which pertains to the objective space, then only one possibility remains. An I cannot be commissioned by an It. An I can receive its call and its warrant only from an I.

18. BELIEF IN THE PERSONAL NATURE OF GOD

All this so far is merely a consequence which follows from the practical attitude of a man upon whom a task is imposed. The basis which this inference affords is still too narrow to carry a belief as weighty as the belief in a living and personal God who holds the entire universe in His power. Belief in the personal God is, indeed, that which is alone able to sustain us through the most desperate hours of this earthly life and in death. The ultimate question, today as always, is whether we really have the right to address prayers to the Power which governs all things as to a Thou who hears our words and with whom we may talk over anything we cannot deal with by ourselves. It is the most burning question of our practical life, whether or not prayer, as Feuerbach supposed, is merely a monologue in which we talk to ourselves and comfort ourselves in order to soothe our nerves, or, as modern psychologists say, a particular form of auto-suggestion which can be understood and rightly assessed only from the point of view of psychotherapy. Since everything depends upon the answer to this question, our belief in the personal nature of God, which is what this question is concerned with, cannot be too firmly consolidated or too carefully secured against the attacks to which we are every day subject.

Anyone who accepts the modern view of the world begins by raising the following weighty objection to the belief in a personal God with whom we communicate by means of prayer. It is, after all, only from our human experience that we know what a personality is. A person is always a being like you or me, in other words a quasi-human being, an animate bodily organism. If, then, we address as a person the Power which underlies all things, that can really be nothing else but a quite primitive anthropomorphism. As Feuerbach shows, man creates for himself with his imagination a reflection of his own wishes and hopes, an idealized representation of what he himself would like to be, and this he projects on to the clouds. The gods of the primitive peoples were idealized tribal chieftains, mighty heroes bursting with energy and endowed with all the emotions and passions. If the civilized man of today personifies the Power which stands above him, this Power is for him merely the embodiment of the ideal conception of a mentally and morally superior man of our own time. Since even the most highly developed human being still belongs to the family of the vertebrates, it follows that God, as Ernst Haeckel on the basis of this assumption quite correctly formulated it, is a 'gaseous vertebrate'. He is thereby drawn down into the domain of the puny beings that people our planet, which itself, as we know today, is like a mere particle of dust in the immensity of the cosmos.

It is not only since Feuerbach but from time immemorial that this devastating objection has been raised against the belief in a personal God. The ingenious defensive tactics with which the theology of an earlier period sought to ward off the attack entirely failed to overcome this objection. One may think, for example, of Albrecht Ritschl's adroit treatment of David Friedrich Strauss's denial of the personal nature of God. And the theology of our own day has been no more successful with its simple appeal to the authority of the revealed Word. But whatever theological standpoint we may adopt, we are in no case entitled to speak in the religious field of the personal nature of God so long as in all other fields of knowledge our conception of the universe is one which excludes this religious proposition. That is the case so long as the human personality, which after all we always have in view when we speak of a person, is for us an *indivisible* whole, a psychophysical organism in which body and soul form an indissoluble unity. In fact it is only from human life that we know the meaning of the word person. But in comparison with the galactic systems, which span thousands of light-years, the planet, which—for what, in terms of the thousands of millions of time-years, is a negligible instant of time—is the scene of our human life, is only a minute speck of dust which appears as insignificant as a grain of sand in the Sahara Desert. How can we be so bold as to take this concept of the person, which we have acquired only within this exiguous and—in comparison with the whole—insignificant range of experience, and apply it without further ado to the Power, hidden from us by a thousand veils, which moves the universe?

There is only one presupposition which can possible render this procedure admissible. We need to have taken the step whereby, as we saw in an earlier chapter, a new epoch is opened in the history of ideas. We need to have perceived that the ego, although we may for the time being know it only in its relation to a minute human body, even in that relation pertains to an entirely different space from that to which the whole objective world pertains. We need to have made the discovery that this ego, even within our narrow human experience, stands as a totally non-objectivisable quantity outside all the measurements and quantitative relations of the objective world. Only if I draw a clear distinction between the two, my own non-objective ego on the one hand,

and on the other hand the destiny which binds me for the duration of my present life to this particular position in the spatial-temporal world, attaching me to a reference body from which there arise quite definite measurements of extension and duration, only then is it at any rate conceivable, and not an inadmissible relapse into the long discarded divine myths of primitive tribes, if we apply the words I and Thou to a Power that lives in the immeasurable dimensions which, as our modern astronomical knowledge shows us, the cosmos possesses. Only when this crucial step has been taken is the concept of the ego and of the personality freed at a single stroke from the tyranny of the infinitesimally minute measurements and quantitative relations within which our human existence is confined. Only then is it at any rate logically possible to apply this concept to the universe as a whole, with its dimensions which infinitely exceed anything that we with the boldest human imagination can possibly visualize.

All this means no more than that belief in the personal nature of the Power which rules the world is at any rate conceivable. What is it, now, that entitles us to take the second step and to venture upon the belief that this possibility is the great reality which may be the underlying principle of our whole life? We are entitled to take this second, crucial step only if the assumption which we have made from the outset in this section is true, namely that the *presence* of God, the side of this Power which is turned towards us—and indeed with our human thinking we can never penetrate into the essential nature of this Power—is in fact a *space*. A space, of course, is not a self-contained whole, with definable boundaries separating it in the objective sense from something else. Such definable limits are the property only of the contents of a space, occupying a location within it, i.e. the persons and things with which the space is filled. But everything there is may always be arranged in a space according to a definite structural principle. This applies quite particularly to the suprapolar space, which also embraces all the other spaces we have so far mentioned. Consequently, if this suprapolar space is found, *all* the circumstances and *all* the relations in which we stand within the polar world are always simultaneously rendered ineffective in the suprapolar space. If this higher space exists at all, then it comes into force all along the line. The new structural order which obtains in the suprapolar space cannot then be limited in its validity to a circumscribed field of reality. On the contrary, it must embrace everything. Thus there is no relation at all in which the 'either or', the clear-cut alternative, within which, in the polar world, this relation is inescapably confined, is not rendered ineffective and overcome in the higher synthesis which in the suprapolar space comes into force all along the line.

In the later parts of this work we shall be obliged to demonstrate this with reference to the most important relations with which modern natural science confronts us, and first and foremost with reference to the causal relation which must always be postulated in every scientific explanation of natural phenomena. We shall see that the causal connexion within the polar world always confines us within the 'either or', the clear-cut alternative between the two possibilities: either a *relativistic* regression through an infinite series of causes and effects, a *regressus in infinitum,* in which we can nowhere come to the ultimate cause for which we are seeking; or else a *positivistic* positing of an original state into the antecedents of which we are unwilling to enquire, for example an original nebular mass, the rotation of which has produced the cosmos. It will be seen that the belief in creation is the suprapolar synthesis whereby in this domain the 'either or', the clear-cut alternative between relativism and positivism, is overcome. It is much the same with the relation of succession within the time-series, with the problem of the ultimate original constituent parts or elementary particles out of which reality is constructed, and with the problem of the reference body which must serve as the basis for the determination of kinetic relations within the universe. But if the structure of the suprapolar space comes into force equally in *all* the relations in which we stand, then this is above all true of the most important relation in which we are involved, the relation between the I and the Thou. This brings us to the question: What bearing has the structure of the suprapolar space on the solution of the riddle of our personal existence?

Before we look for a solution of this problem we must first exactly formulate the question which is to be answered. We must distinguish the question we are discussing here from the other question with which it has over and over again been confused. We are not speaking here of the problem of how mentally endowed personalities come into being within the historical and biological causal nexus of the world. There is no doubt at all that not only the form of the bodily organisms but also the mental conformation of every human individual has quite definite genetic causes, and that in the shaping of them the entire genetic complexes of the father and the mother combine in accordance with the Mendelian laws. Goethe says, as we all know, that:

> From my father I get my stature and my earnestness in the conduct of my life.
> From my little mother I get my cheerful nature and my delight in telling stories.

Yet not only in the case of a poet like Goethe, but even in the case of the most insignificant average individual, these two causal series, the paternal one and the maternal one, produce their combined effect in the germ plasm. In addition to these there are the thousands of different influences of the historical events under the impact of which a man may grow up, and the atmosphere in his family and in the school through which he passes. But the historical and biological problem, which the emergence of every thinking personality repeatedly poses, is not the problem with which we are concerned in the present context. The unfathomable riddle of the Sphinx with which my personal existence confronts me is to be found rather in quite a different question, the question of why, amid the immense abundance and multiplicity of personalities which spring from the fertile soil of this earth like the flowers from a springtime meadow on a day in May, this one particular personality should be assigned to me as the rôle which I must assume and which I must play out to the bitter end. Why am I not Goethe, or any other one of the circle of leading men in that great period of history? Why have I been born as a member of a ruined nation in this time of pettiness and meanness? Of course, it does not in any way affect the objective causal nexus, which is the concern of natural science and historical research, whether it has fallen to my lot to be born in the twentieth century or in the eighteenth century. So the objective world can simply give me no answer to the question of where I come from and why the 'there' into which I am 'cast' lies at precisely this point and not at some other point. Consequently it cannot be from the objective world that this mysterious determining of my position derives.

On one point Fichte was certainly right. An I cannot be placed by an It. An I can be placed only by an I. But the I which places me cannot, as Fichte supposed, be myself. For in that case I should necessarily be able to extinguish myself again, and, in the words of Hamlet's soliloquy, 'myself might my quietus make with a bare bodkin'. I should be able to exchange myself for another who was born under a happier constellation. But that I cannot do. I can kill my body but I cannot 'make the quietus' of my self; I have no power over my self. Nor can the authority which has placed me, and which is repeatedly placing me anew, be any other member of the infinite series of reciprocally conditioned subjects which are linked together in the I-Thou space. For always, whenever within this world of the encounters I find my Thou, the soul which redeems me from my I-solitude and which is responsive to my words, the very reason why this encounter affords me such relief and happiness is that this Thou falls into my lap as a gift from above and without any intervention on my part. When I have this experience it becomes overwhelmingly clear to me that I cannot myself create the Thou which confronts me. I have no power over its existence, just as I have no power over myself. And just as I cannot create the Thou, so too the Thou cannot create me. Consequently, within the space of the encounters, too, there can be no Thou which might have created me and placed me at this point at which I stand.

Let us sum up what has been said, so that we may draw the final consequence from it. The authority which has placed me cannot be an It. Nor can this authority be I myself. Nor can this authority be any Thou, i.e. any other ego within the polar I-Thou series. From all this there follows the inescapable consequence that: *Either* there is no answer at all to the question of where I come from. The placing of my ego, in which is implied the whole destiny of my life with all its sorrows and joys, is an absolutely insoluble riddle. The word 'destiny', which is usually applied here, is far too lofty a term; for now the placing of my ego is quite a ridiculous matter of chance; I have been cast up by a tidal wave at some completely fortuitous spot on the shore of the world. *Or else* the authority which places me is an I. But this I cannot be governed by the law of polarity. It cannot be a link in the interminable polar I-Thou series. It must be suprapolar. If, then, we wish to venture any assertion at all with regard to this I, we must proceed here according to the same rule which we applied in our approach to the problem of the warrant for our actions, when we determined the authority from which alone we can receive a mission which raises us above the domain of the polar space. If the I from which we receive our existence is suprapolar, then its existence lies outside and above the two alternatives which within the polar world-form, and consequently also within the polar series of the encounters, are always the only ones possible. The I to which we are here led breaks down the 'Either/Or' between relativism and positivism all along the line. The I before which I stand here must not describe its existence, as you and I do, with the relativistic assertion: I am this one, but I might just as well be some other; I stand here, but I might just as well stand at some other position. Nor can this I say of itself, in accordance with the second, the positivistic possibility; I myself have placed myself, and I myself place myself over and over again from moment to moment anew. The existence of this I transcends these two alternatives, which within the polar world are alone possible.

This third possibility, in which the 'Either/Or' of the polar world is resolved in a higher synthesis, is clearly displayed to us in the Bible, already in the Old Testament. At the great moment when God gave Moses the allotted task for his people, the moment which gave the history of this people its direction for all time, He summed up His Name in the words 'I am that I am' or 'I shall be that I shall be' (Ex. 4.14). That is to say: My being rests upon itself. I do not need to place myself. I am from eternity; and what I have been from eternity, that shall I be unto eternity. Spinoza was trying to express this suprapolar being of God, of which the Bible speaks, when he defined the absolute substance in the words *substantia illa quae nullius aliae substantiae eget ad subsistendum*, that substance which requires no other substance in order to exist. To the eternal I, which rests upon itself and which therefore in the proper sense of the word alone truly *is*, we may say in our prayers: 'Before the mountains were brought forth, or ever thou hadst formed the earth and the world, even from everlasting to everlasting, thou *art* God' (Ps. 90.2). 'It is he that hath made us, and not we ourselves' (Ps. 100.3). If at every instant I take my existence, and my being placed at this point in the world, directly from His hand, then I find the sanction for my life and I am founded upon eternity. I am freed from the paralysing sense of the fortuitousness and the arbitrariness of my being 'cast' into this situation. I acquire the certainty that, even though from the polar point of view, this placing of me is neither logically nor causally necessary, yet it follows from a suprapolar necessity which is contrary to all polar necessities. It carries within it a sacred obligation. Not only does this mean that I am set free from the relativistic sense of fortuitousness; I am freed at the same time from the convulsed condition in which I was endeavouring to establish myself positivistically and to render myself absolute. The incessant movement is stilled by dint of which I was trying to find the Thou to which I can devote myself wholly. I rest effortlessly in Him who alone can say of Himself 'I am that I am'. But the necessity of this determining of my existence, in which all questions 'Why?' are resolved, is not disclosed to me in the theoretical attitude of a spectator, but always only when I at the same time act under the impulsion of an inner mission which bears within itself the same suprapolar necessity. Together with the command under which I stand, the situation, too, in which I receive this command, becomes sacred to me, however

difficult and intolerable this situation in life may appear to
me; and my own ego, which receives this command, thereby
moves, even in a situation which seems totally meaningless,
into the light of eternity.

Several simple consequences may be drawn from this with
regard to our relation to God. God is not an It, since no I
could be generated from an It. And so God can never, as is
always possible in the case of an It, be the object of my action,
which I may confront in the attitude of an onlooker in order
to examine it microscopically or to record it photographically.
So long as I endeavour, as a cool, scientific observer, to discover God from the effects which He produces, I see nothing
of God. There can be no meeting with Him. Nor can I find
God by immersing myself in myself, the approach which has
been tried over and over again, in Fichte's cult of the ego and
in the Oriental redemption religions. The mystics supposed
that if I completely immerse myself in myself there opens up,
as it were, a pit within me into which I can sink down until
I come to the bottom where I am identical with all beings.
As has no doubt been most clearly recognized by Ferdinand
Ebner, by this mystical path, by immersing myself in myself,
I can never free myself from my desperate I-solitude. I can
find God only if He meets me as my Thou. But this cannot
be a Thou encounter such as is possible in the space of the
polar Thou encounters. In the polytheistic religions, which
grew up at the primitive stage of the polar, three-dimensional
space, man communicates with the gods as with beings of his
own kind. They confront him either as dangerous adversaries, with whom one must fight or conclude a treaty of
mutual assistance, or else as allies, who can be treated as
friends and equals. All intercourse between man and God
remains analagous to the intercourse between man and man,
and is precisely on that account subject to the limitation which
governs all intercourse between the I and the Thou within
the polar space. Neither of us can see into the other. We are
shut off from one another by an opaque wall. That is what
underlies all the tragic tensions, conflicts and mutual mis-
understandings which arise between us. We see one another
always only from without and never from within. Each of us,

with the help of the well-known method of analogical inference, deduces from the vital utterances of the other conclusions regarding the hidden inner world which perhaps lies
behind these utterances. I may indeed endeavour with love
and sympathy to put myself in your position. If I have any
imagination, I can to some extent enter into your mind and
visualize your point of view. But I can never really transpose
myself into your situation. There is always the impenetrable
wall between us. This impenetrable wall which separates us
is the intractable 'Either/Or' relation. Either I am person A
and must see the world from this centre; in which case I cannot at the same time be any one of the other persons, B, C or
D, each of whom necessarily sees everything from some different central point. Or else I am one of the others, in which
case I cannot be this one. There is no third possibility.

God is the suprapolar Thou which breaks down this Either/
Or' which encloses us all with its presence. He stands above
and beyond the mutual exclusiveness which divides us. We
can illustrate this by an analogy. There are prisons of a
modern design in which each cell is open at the top. As a
result of this, the chief warder can look into all the cells from
above, while the prisoners are unable to see one another
because they are separated by the cell walls. In the same way
God looks down directly into the inside of us, while we are
unable to look into one another. God alone transcends the
opposition between the many possible positions in space and
time in which by a fatal necessity we have been irrevocably
situated since the time of our birth. I cannot look into God.
'God dwelleth in the light which no man can approach unto'
(I Tim. 6.16). But God sees into me. 'Thou compassest my
path and my lying down, and understandest my thought afar
off.' Here we have an entirely new and unique I-Thou relation, one which is fundamentally different from the attitude
of the onlooker and scientific observer, from the mystical
immersion of myself in myself, and from the Thou encounter
with a fellow human being which in the polytheistic religions
is extended to include intercourse with the gods. This new
and unique relation is prayer. Prayer stills the incessant
movement of my quest for a Thou to whom I can devote my-

self wholly. God is the omnipresent Thou of every I, the Being who is immediately close to us, before whom we all stand always, before whom we do all our deeds, and before whom we think even our most secret thoughts. It is He who listens to our most secret conversations with ourselves, and who never misunderstands us. Jesus says: 'The Father knoweth what things we have need of, before we ask him.' God is therefore 'the Father of all spirits', 'of whom the whole family in heaven and earth is named' (Eph. 3.15).

When we were considering the problem of the sanction for our activity, we saw that the 'holy necessity', which rests upon everyone who is commissioned by God, is a synthesis between the infinite variety of possibilities with which the whole world is full, and amid which the relativist loses his way, and the restrictedness of the positivist, for whom only one course of action is possible. The synthesis lay in the fact that the man who was sent by God was aware that he must do the one deed which at this cosmic instant was unconditionally necessary in accordance with the meaning of the universe as a whole. In a similar way the presence of God is a synthesis between the universality of all the ego-beings (*die Allheit aller Ichwesen*) which the whole cosmos comprises and the solitude of the individual ego which is shut off from all other egos. In the presence of God all the egos which the universe comprises are contained together; for all stand in His presence, all live at every moment before Him. And yet the presence of God is not the removal of all ego-distinctions; it does not mean that, near to God, all egos are merged in one another and lose their identity in one another. God is, on the contrary, the Individual who reveals Himself to each individual one of us in our profound solitude as our own particular Thou to whom we may say in our prayers 'My God . . .' Consequently I can never stand in a private relation to God. When I come before God in prayer, all other ego-beings are, in a mysterious manner, also present. By way of God I am linked with all the beings the universe contains. When I stand before God they are all my brothers, even though within the polar space I am divided from them by insurmountable walls. I am standing always before Him whose will and cosmic plan encompasses all beings, holding them aloft above the abyss of non-existence, no matter whether they flee from Him, or seek Him, or have already found Him. For this reason, even in my most solitary prayer in my secret chamber, I come in spirit together with all beings to meet the One before whom we all stand. That is why prayer has a universal character. Intercession has a world-embracing horizon. I cannot come before God without being aware of my responsibility for all those with whom I belong together, as a member of my nation, as a member of mankind, and as a member of the whole animate universe. 'I exhort therefore,' says the apostle, 'that, first of all, supplications, prayers, intercessions, and giving of thanks be made for all men' (I Tim. 2.1).

We see, therefore, that if God is, then, in the domain of the I-Thou relation too, the 'Either/Or' between positivism and relativism, in which within the space of polarity we were confined, is broken down and bridged over by suprapolar means. Only thus do all the relations in which we stand with respect to one another receive their eternal foundation and their final consummation. The friendship between the I and the Thou achieves its consummation only when God is the invisible Third in whose presence we both stand, the invisible point of intersection through which all the lines must pass which run, this way and that, between us. Marriage is happy only if both husband and wife are sustained by God, so that each is able to support and uphold the other. One human being can receive the confidence of another, and be a person to whom he can speak his mind unreservedly and in all situations, only if he accepts a priestly responsibility for him before God. If that is not the case, then he lacks all pastoral authority and the whole relation of trust rests only on a human power of suggestion which he exerts upon the other. This power of suggestion may at any moment fail if the veil is torn and the other sees that it was all a mere deception. Thus all the relations in which human beings afford one another mutual support always rest solely on the fact that God sustains them all, because He is the ultimate Thou of them all. All true relations of confidence between human beings are governed by the principle *teneo quia teneor*: I hold because I am held. If

God is eliminated, from whom in pure passivity we receive our ultimate support, then our human community is like the 'Fall of the Damned' in Rubens' painting, where a multitude of human figures clasp one another and cling to one another in the vain hope that they may be able to halt this descent into the bottomless gulf into which they are all together being irresistibly drawn. But when the unceasing movement which impels the I towards the Thou has been stilled in God, then we know that the 'ultimate reality' that stands above us cannot be an impersonal power, an It, a destiny or a fate, to which we can only resign ourselves in silence, but must be an I, which we may properly address as Thou. Indeed fatalism, wherever it has arisen, in Greek tragedy, in the later period of the ancient Germanic polytheism and again in our own time, has always been merely the form assumed by a dying religion shortly before it has become extinct. In fatalism the obscure feeling is still alive that we are not alone by ourselves but that there is a Power standing above us. But this Power can no longer be addressed. It is a dark fatality, of which we have become the victims and which we can only accept in silence. That is the last remnant which is left, in periods of decline, of the belief in God or in gods: it is a mere residue. In fatalism the religious life flares up for one last time before sinking into the all-consuming ocean of materialism and atheism and being extinguished for ever. For this reason fatalism can never inspire strength for the struggle of life. This strength can come only from union with the personal God, who hears us when we call upon Him in our need and in whom we can put our trust.

If the omnipresent Power, which governs all things absolutely, is not a blind destiny but a Thou with which all ego-beings may enter into direct communication, then this fact resolves the disharmony which runs through the whole world and of which we spoke in our summing-up at the end of Chapter 10. This disharmony, as we then saw, arises from the 'Either/Or' which even in the non-objective space divides the I from the Thou and generates an electric tension between them which is subsequently projected from there on to the objective plane and here discharged in a terrible explosion in the struggles which convulse the world. The 'Either/Or', by which the I and the Thou are hermetically sealed off from one another so that neither can see directly into the other's inner being, now gives rise to that desperate I-loneliness (*Icheinsamkeit*) which weighs oppressively upon all the ego-beings that fill the universe. Hermann Hesse in one of his poems compares the passage of the ego-beings through life with the wandering of human beings through a fog which is so dense that although they are all walking together they cannot see one another. 'Neither sees the other; each walks alone, alone.'

But if God is 'the Father of all spirits', the eternal Thou of all beings, then, as we have seen, all the walls of this monstrous many-celled prison are at one stroke rendered ineffective from above. For then there exists an I which sees simultaneously into all the cells just as directly as we see each into our own ego (and that is all we can see directly). This 'Cosmic Ego' (*Weltall-Ich*) is the meeting-point through which all the beings which are shut off from one another may enter into direct communication with one another. In this way our mutual relations with one another are fundamentally transformed. If there is no personal God, then it is by a ridiculous coincidence that each one of us has been 'cast' into the position at which he must stand until the bitter end. He is alone by himself in this position; he fights alone, suffers alone, and dies alone. The contents of his own consciousness-space are his only possessions. He is, as Max Stirner said, 'the only one and his property'. If I possess only myself and all others are fundamentally quite alien to me and remote from me, then the only possible attitude is ethical solipsism. The others do not concern me at all; for they are beyond me and beyond the little world which alone belongs to me and which alone is accessible to me. 'Am I my brother's keeper?' I can only be cold towards the others, hate them if they harm me, envy them if they are more fortunate than I am, and look on indifferently if things go ill with them. But if God exists, through whom the cell walls between us are rendered ineffective, then the whole relation between you and me is fundamentally altered. Then I know that you, like me, were not 'cast' by a blind chance into the position at which you stand. God, who placed us both, and before whom we both stand, has allotted to each of us the position at which he is stationed. He might equally well have put you in my position and me in yours. He might equally well have assigned to me the body which He has given to you as an instrument, with its manifold debilities and its inherited pathological conditions. In that case it is I who would have to play on the world's stage the rôle which you are now obliged to play out to the end. You would find me as hard to endure as I now find you. As soon as this has become clear to me in the presence of God, there arises a new relation between you and me. I distinguish your self, your 'soul', from the destiny which God has imposed upon you, just as I distinguish my own self, my own 'soul', from the temporary rôle which God has assigned to me for this brief lifetime. In this way our souls move together into a new community which is possible only in the presence of God. We can no longer go on living side by side, coldly, as strangers and without pity. However difficult it may be for us to live peaceably together, as creatures of God we are responsible for one another. We bear one another's burdens. This is the new relation between the I and the Thou, and it is expressed most clearly when we pray together. It is what is meant in the New Testament by the term 'brotherly love' (ἀγάπη).

A particularly striking example of the fundamental change which takes place in one who abandons philosophical pantheism and fatalism and encounters the personal God is afforded by the experience, during the first world war, of the poet, Max Dauthendey, to whom we have already referred. Far away in the South Seas he had been cut off by the outbreak of the war from his homeland and from his wife. The philosophical idea of God, on the basis of which he had hitherto conducted his life, could not give him the strength to accept this destiny and to master his despair. And then there took place the miracle which he describes in his diary, writing on the 30th of June, 1917, in the solitude of the Tengger Mountains in Eastern Java. 'This morning, after reading the fiftieth and sixtieth Psalms of David, I realized some-

thing. I realized that there is a *personal* God. Three weeks
before my fiftieth birthday I received this revelation, which
since I was twenty—thirty years long—I had been worrying
over, doubting, pursuing, and striving for. What a glorious
certainty of purpose has today entered into my heart, my mind
and my body! God lives and is personal as all lives through
Him.' The jubilation, into which the poet breaks out after
this all-transforming realization, shows especially clearly that
he has thereby discovered a completely new space, a space in
which he sees everything—even the whole of nature and the
whole destiny of man—with new eyes. 'The whole of life is
a festal procession ordered by God, and at the head of the line
there goes God Himself as a Personality. . . . The I of the
World is God. . . !' The philosophers' impersonal idea of
God now appears to him as a state of twilight semi-conscious-
ness—'as all educated thinkers nowadays consider themselves
enlightened with their doubts and twilight dimness'. Now
the whole fog of indefinite presentiments of God has left him.
The reality of God has taken on clear outlines for his intellect
too. 'There is a purpose in it all. I feel as though the dirt
had all at once been washed away from my eyes, my mind, my
heart, my body, my courage, and my joy in life. . . . I thank
Thee, Divine I (*Gottes-Ich*), that before my death and after
thirty years of seeking I have perceived Thee with my understanding and that I may now live unto Thee with wonder.
Man! Dauthendey! Be joyful!' The certitude of the personal nature of God now all at once gives him the strength to
overcome the despair from which pantheism and fatalism had
been unable to free him. The hard fate of having to die far
from his homeland and of being unable to see his wife again
is one which he can now accept quietly and thankfully from
the hand of the personal God. 'Even if I am to die here, I
will still be glad that all my torment has had an inner purpose.
For to know of the personal nature of God is a *far* more blessed
thing than to know of the festal nature of the universe. Now
God, too, stands before me as a joy in the life of the universe.
Some day perhaps I shall see Him from person to person with
my outward eyes too, just as I have now seen and recognized
him with my inward eyes.'

19. NATURAL LAW, THE ORDER OF CREATION, AND GUILT

Our chapter on the personal nature of God has made us particularly clearly aware of something which had already been shown by the preceding chapters, namely, that ultimately there is only one question upon the answer to which everything depends and to which all the fundamental problems of our thought and life may be reduced. This is the question whether there in fact exists that suprapolar space of which we have repeatedly spoken in all these chapters, or whether this suprapolar space is an illusion, so that we are confined within the polar space with all our perceptions, conceptions and cogitations. We are confronted here with an 'Either/Or', a clear-cut alternative between two possibilities, and on the decision which must be taken will depend the answer to all the other questions. We will now compare these two possibilities by briefly summing up once again the conclusions which follow from the previous chapters in this section.

The first possibility is this. There is a suprapolar space in which we stand together with all the rest of reality. From this there follow four inescapable consequences.

Firstly, there is a personal God, who rules all things and in whose omnipresence all beings stand. This follows simply from the circumstance that the suprapolar region is an omnipresent space, so that its structural form must quite necessarily apply also to the I-Thou relation. This leads on to the eternal Thou, before whom we all stand.

Secondly, each one of us receives his personal existence, and the position at which he is placed in this world, directly from God. Kierkegaard is right when he says: 'Belief consists in my basing myself perspicuously on Him who has placed me.'

Thirdly, there is a sanction for our action, a commission from God, in which I can rest effortlessly, and supported by which I can defy the whole world. For what the New Testament says of Christ is in fact true, namely that He has the divine authority to be the way, the truth and the life for all them that put their trust in Him.

Fourthly, behind the whole course of the world and the

process of nature, despite all apparent evidence to the contrary and in spite of everything which seems to us meaningless and incomprehensible, there must be a plan which derives from a universal mind or spirit (*All-Geist*). The course of the world must be directed towards a final goal, which is now still concealed from us.

The other possibility is this. The suprapolar space is an illusion and we are inescapably confined, with all our thoughts and actions, within the polar space. From this there follow the four contrary consequences.

Firstly, there is no personal God, but only an impersonal fate. Prayer is only a monologue or a form of auto-suggestion. Each one of us is entirely alone with himself and his destiny.

Secondly, my personal existence, together with the fact of my being placed at this position where I am obliged to fight out my struggle with life to the end, is a meaningless coincidence. It is in fact as Tolstoy saw it when he became aware of the immensity and the endlessness of the cosmic space and the cosmic process, in which no origin and no goal are anywhere to be found, such as might invest the whole with a meaning. In his *Confession* he sums up his state of mind at this juncture in the words: 'This life is nothing but a stupid, mischievous joke which someone has taken the liberty of playing on me. Although I did not acknowledge the existence of a "someone" who could have created me, this was nevertheless quite the most natural form in which I could visualize the matter—the idea that someone had amused himself by playing a malicious and stupid joke on me when he put me into the world.'

Thirdly, there is no sanction for our activity. Either I must select at random from the multitude of values one which happens to please me, and throw it away again when I am bored with it. Or else I must on my own authority determine a permanent goal for my life. If some people have believed themselves to be acting in accordance with a higher 'mission', this was merely the psychological form in which they had worked themselves up into an *idée fixe*.

Fourthly, the whole process of nature is a meaningless interplay of forces, in which the weaker is always devoured by the stronger. The entire evolution of the organic world consists, as Schopenhauer represents it in his pessimistic reflections on nature, solely in the emergence upon the restricted surface of the earth of ever new species of plants and animals which are filled with the meaningless impulse to reproduce and proliferate endlessly and unrestrainedly, so that within this narrow space there must arise a murderous struggle for existence, transforming the world into a hell.

We have now confronted and contrasted the two possibilities between which we have to decide. With either of these two possible underlying attitudes the structure of the spaces in which reality is seen immediately brings into effect all the consequences which follow in each case from the respective overall conception of reality. Against this attempt to reduce our situation, despite its apparent complexity, to a simple 'Either/Or', there arises the following obvious objection. Does not our spatial-temporal world of experience, although it has the form of polarity, nevertheless afford us quite definite indications of the proper direction for our activity, investing our existence with a clear meaning, without our having recourse to mysterious 'tasks' and commissions from a suprapolar region? One may consider particularly the 'natural law', the 'orders of creation', and the voice of conscience, which makes itself heard inescapably in the consciousness of guilt. We must now very briefly discuss the three new factors which this objection introduces, and relate them to the conclusions to which we have been led in the preceding chapters.

We must begin with a few words about the old controversy which still continues today between the supporters of *natural law* and the legal positivists. It is an undeniable fact that there is a law 'which is born with us', a law which expresses itself involuntarily in the mind of every human being even before the appearance of human legal institutions and written statutes. Among all nations, especially in our own time, there arises the cry for justice, for equal rights for all, and for a just distribution of property. In every human being there lives a natural sense of justice, which demands condign punishment for violations of the law. Even in a group of schoolchildren, playing together in the school yard, there spontaneously comes into being a rule or code which has the force of law and to which all must conform if they do not wish to be excluded from the society of their playfellows. But this undeniable fact does not in itself, as is often assumed, lead us out beyond the relativeness of all phenomena pertaining to the polar space. For this natural law, which we encounter here, is merely the outward aspect of the existence of a supra-individual sociological structure, which is built up on a particular pattern and in accordance with definite rules and in which we as individuals find ourselves placed already by virtue of our birth within a family and a nation and state. But this social structure is a relative quantity; it has become and it can vanish again. It is the product of a long biological and historical process of evolution, which began already in the animal world, for example in the states of the bees and ants, and then led upwards to the form of society which we find in the most highly developed human state. I instinctively perceive the relative character of this form of community, and of all the notions of natural law which follow from it, as soon as this legal order is imperilled by opposing forces and I am called upon to sacrifice my life in order to preserve it. Consider, for example, the system of private ownership, to which we in Europe have been accustomed for thousands of years, or the venerable monarchic constitution under which the older ones of us in Germany grew up from our childhood on. When I am called upon to sacrifice my life for a political constitution or a system of property-distribution of this kind, I feel at once that, admittedly, already by my birth I have been integrated into these orders of human collective life, and that they are deeply engrained in me, so that my 'natural sense of justice' has, by way of the 'collective subconscious', been conditioned and shaped by them; yet all this is not nearly enough to attach me to them so unconditionally that I am prepared to die in a forlorn hope in order to preserve them. For this absolute obligation to take effect, something more must be added, something which, quite independently of all occurrences within the spatial-temporal world, binds me to these orders for ever with my whole existence. That which exerts upon us this unconditionally binding power cannot emanate from the polar space. It must pertain to the suprapolar space. Upon the temporal facts of these particular social and political orders there must fall an accent from eternity which raises them above all that is temporal and invests them with an eternal significance.

We can visualize the matter most clearly by considering the old monarchic form of the state in Japan, which rested on the belief that the Mikado was descended from the Sun Goddess. Over and over again highly educated Japanese, and especially historians at the Imperial University, ventured very cautiously to express the idea that this myth is, of course, no more than the symbolic representation of the glorious history of the Japanese people and the consciousness of its invincibility. In other words, they endeavoured to explain in terms of the polar space and events within it the unconditional obligation of every Japanese to sacrifice his life for the Mikado. But this attempt to explain was always forcibly suppressed; for it was instinctively felt that this polar explanation meant undermining the foundation upon which rested the unrestricted readiness of every Japanese to sacrifice himself for his people. From this example we see that a system or order of life, a monarchic state, for example, however firmly it may be rooted in long habituation and a millennium of history, still possesses the power to command unconditional adherence only if the same facts, which within the polar space by virtue of a long development have become historic, stand simultaneously and as such in the suprapolar space, and from there receive the accent of eternity. If this accent is lacking, which we cannot ourselves impart and which must always have been received from a higher dimension, then any legal order will always remain merely a relative and time-conditioned phenomenon, even though it was 'born with us' and even though it finds expression in our natural sense of justice.

Similar to our attitude to 'natural law' must be our attitude to that concept of the 'orders of creation' which is the object of so much dispute today especially amongst theologians, a concept upon which it is possible to construct a 'natural theology'. Here, again, we are confronted in the first place by a body of indubitable facts. The natural order which renders children completely dependent on their parents during the first years of their lives, the order which brings husband and wife into a quite definite natural relation to one another, is not established by man. It is an ' original order' (*Urordnung*), into which we were born already as children. For we do not come into the world as adults, but as small, help-less creatures, which without their parents would necessarily perish. It is the same with the order of marriage. For we are not born as sexless human beings, but as men and women, standing with respect to one another in a relation which derives from the nature of the creation. As the defenders of the ' orders of creation' rightly point out, our Lord, in dealing with the question of divorce, goes back beyond the Law of Moses to the ' beginning of the creation' when God made man-kind ' male and female' (Mark. 10.6). But even this fact, with which we find ourselves confronted already when we are born, does not in itself lead us beyond relativism. So long as we consider these natural orders in terms of the polar world-evolution they are never more than phases in the general biological evolution of the organic world, phases which have arisen from earlier levels of development. In the case of fish, the young separate themselves from their parents as soon as they are born; in the case of birds, after a short period of parental care in the nest, as soon as they are fledged. If at the human stage of development children are dependent on their parents for a longer time, from the biological point of view this is due solely to the fact that human offspring develop more slowly and therefore need longer before they are able to take up the struggle for existence independently.

Christ refers to the archetypal form of the human sexual partnership as being, in accordance with the design of the creation, the first state of man as he now is (Mark 10.6), and yet, so far as we know today, even this only emerged gradually in the course of a long biological process of development from the still half-bestial early stage of matriarchal and patriarchal polygamy. Consequently, so long as our thoughts are still confined within the polar space, we can only regard the order of marriage, which is now predominant amongst mankind, as

one among the many relative forms of sexual partnership
which in the course of time have developed and vanished
again only to make way for others. I can recognize it as the
'original order', revealing the eternal meaning of sexual life,
only when, under the influence of Jesus, I have, at the innermost point of my existence, perceived both the eternal value
of every human soul and the suprapolar space. It is only
when, by my perceiving the suprapolar space, my eyes have
been opened to the eternal meaning of my existence, that the
accent of eternity falls upon this particular form of sexual
partnership and I understand the pregnant words which
Christ quotes here from the chapter of the creation: 'And
God created man . . . male and female created he them'
(Gen. 1.27). Monogamy, then, seen in the light of the suprapolar space, is a form of life instituted by the *personal* God
before whom we stand, and it is from this fact that it derives
an eternal significance. As soon as a nation loses the belief
in the personal God, who has laid the accent of eternity on
precisely this form of sexual partnership and has sanctified it
as an indissoluble union, this nation's sexual life quite necessarily sinks back unchecked into the bestial stage of development. Marriage is then no more than a contract which can
at any time be immediately revoked, as soon as the two
partners are no longer inclined to remain together.

The eternal archetypal space (*Urraum*) is perceived always
only from the central point at which contact is established
between the great historical and biological nexuses on the one
hand and my own personal ego in its present oppressive situation on the other hand. This renders intelligible a further
important point, to which Pascual Jordan alludes in the essay
which we have already cited. This is the consciousness of
responsibility and of *guilt*. It has, of course, long since become customary to employ the words 'debt' and 'guilt' in a
sense in which they have lost their original metaphysical meaning. The word 'debt' is employed in a purely commercial
sense in speaking of a sum of money which one has still to pay
to a creditor. One speaks of legal guilt when someone has
contravened an ordinance of the state, of political guilt when
a nation has failed politically at some fateful moment of its

P

history, and of moral guilt which may be incurred even on the basis of a non-religious ethic. But in its strict sense the word 'guilt', like the word 'conscience', with which it is intimately connected, always has a metaphysical connotation. To borrow Jaspers' term, it signifies 'metaphysical guilt'. The sense of guilt, the accusing voice of conscience, is with many people the last remnant that is left them of the metaphysical substrata of our existence, even after they have long since lost their belief in the personal God. This has given rise to the erroneous opinion that conscience is a psychological faculty which even in the polar space is in any case present in every human being, so that it is still always possible to appeal to the conscience even of an atheist. But that is to overlook the dividing-line which cannot be crossed. The truth is that we have no right even to pronounce the words 'conscience' and 'awareness of guilt' so long as the suprapolar space is still concealed from us. For to do so can only be to misuse these pregnant words and to falsify their meaning. Goethe says somewhere that consciousness of guilt is the 'kingly crown of mankind'. In the period of German history which lies behind us we have seen that this kingly crown falls from our heads and is lost in the dirt as soon as man no longer has anything above him. There is no need to waste words on that subject. Why must that be so? So long as man's horizon is restricted to this polar world, in which there rages the brutal and unscrupulous struggle for existence between individual human beings and between nations, there is no longer anything to which we can feel ourselves responsible and before which we can experience a sense of guilt. All the old words, such as conscience, guilt, remorse, expiation and forgiveness, are struck out of the dictionary. There remain only two values which are still current coin when all the rest has gone. One of these values is power, which is the sole aim in this world; and the other value is pleasure, which is freely enjoyed by the victor in the struggle for power, who by his victory has secured the place in the sun from which the others are now excluded. Good is what is 'useful', i.e. what helps me to achieve power. Bad is that which weakens me, i.e. that by which my rise to power is impeded.

Why is the concept of guilt immediately lost, together with all the concepts connected with this principle, whenever we are confined within the polar space of temporality? It is because within the polar space every value-magnitude by which I direct my course in the decision of the present moment must, according to everything that has been said so far, be either a *relativum* or a *positum*. In neither case can the reality which demands my allegiance arouse in me a feeling of guilt. Let us begin by considering the first case. The value to which I have given my allegiance, a nation or a civilization or a social order for example, is a relative, temporally restricted magnitude. This value has become effective only by dint of supplanting other relative magnitudes which were formerly prevalent, such as the ideal of a primitive state of nature or a supra-national ideal of humanity. And it, too, will vanish when it is supplanted by other relative magnitudes, when, for example—a thought which looms large in our minds today—the whole of mankind is swept away within a few hours by some all-destroying cosmic cataclysm and disappears from view almost completely. Now, it is possible for me to inflict damage on a relative value-magnitude of this kind. I can undermine its prestige, obstruct its progress, and contribute to its downfall. So long as this relative magnitude is in power, that has very serious consequences for me. It may lead to my losing my life or being pilloried as an ' enemy of the state' or a 'traitor to my country'. But if, in the course of the polar world-process, this value-magnitude is supplanted by some other force, the resistance which I opposed to it may be recognized as heroism and martyrdom. This means that within the world of the polar space, within the framework of relativism, the same action may be from one point of view treason and from the other point of view honourable resistance. Consequently, so long as relativism prevails, it is altogether impossible to speak of *guilt*. This concept cannot arise at all; my conscience can never accuse me if I have done something which from one particular standpoint admittedly seems wrong but which from another standpoint, which I may equally well adopt, is perfectly right. In other words, on the basis of pure relativism, there is no such thing as guilt. I may, of course, act foolishly. I may have backed the wrong horse. I may have been so improvident as to give my allegiance to a cause the downfall of which I might have foreseen. I may be annoyed at having miscalculated. But my *conscience* cannot accuse me on this account. Nor can this give rise to an awareness of guilt.

In the face of this slump in all ethical values, which always results from relativism, and of the unscrupulousness which produces such devastating effects in all fields of human social life, attempts have been made to remedy this 'turning sickness' of relativistic thought by having recourse to *positivism*. But it has been found that it is impossible, by means of a *positum* posited by man himself, to re-awaken the consciousness of guilt when once it has sunk into sleep. Certainly, as a human being I may in fact impose a law upon myself by an act of autonomy. I may resolve in a period of relativism to offer resistance in my own small way to the ever-increasing immorality and moral 'softening of the bones'. I may decide, for example, to impose upon myself the law of absolute conjugal fidelity. In peaceful times this noble resolution may keep me above water; but as soon as my marriage passes through a severe crisis and I am beset by the temptation to cut myself free from all my difficulties by means of the rapid divorce which is so characteristic of our time, I find at once that, even if in a youthful burst of ethical idealism I have determined to abide by the law of marital loyalty, I still cannot feel that I have incurred guilt if now, as a more mature man, I abandon this attitude again. For in this critical situation I become clearly aware of the fact that a law which I have imposed upon myself I can also at any time myself repeal. I cannot impose upon myself any unconditional obligation and responsibility. The violation of a law can weigh upon my conscience as a guilty action, and I can in fact incur guilt with respect to this law, only if this law is not a resolution of my own, a decision which is under my control and which, if the need arose, I could at any time revoke; only, that is to say, if this law emanates from an authority which is superior to me and over which, therefore, I have no control, an authority whose decision I cannot on my own account in any way alter.

It is only against this authority which is superior to me that I can commit sin. Such an authority which is superior to me cannot be conceived within the polar space. For, indeed, any other human being standing within this space, and any supra-individual group of human beings belonging to this space, can enact laws, can, that is to say, establish a *positum* by which I may direct my course; but the situation of this group is precisely the same as my own situation as an individual. Any decree enacted by men can also be repealed and rescinded by men. Any human organized force may compel me, so long as it is in power, to place myself in its service; but it cannot, so long as it remains confined within the polar space, arouse any consciousness of guilt in me if I refuse to obey it.

What follows from all this? All the archetypal words (*Urworte*) of which we have spoken, guilt, responsibility, pangs of conscience, repentance and atonement, belong to the same domain as do the words vocation, task, mission, holy necessity, sanction and inner authority. Within the polar space all these words are entirely absent and totally inaccessible. If they are employed at all in this space they quite properly appear as cases of atavism or relapse into a state of mind which has been superseded. Or else they are re-interpreted psychologically and pathologically as symptoms of morbid degeneration or as an inferiority complex resulting from racial cross-breeding. But these archetypal words at once spring into existence at a single stroke and press in upon us inescapably as soon as the violence of some mysterious upheaval bursts open the prison gates of the polar space.

But when even only one of these words is uttered, we thereby find ourselves in a space which encompasses everything and through which every relation in which we stand is brought into the light of a new synthesis whereby the 'Either/Or' alternative between relativism and positivism is bridged over and surmounted. But, as we have seen, in the suprapolar space, together with all the other relations, it is especially the Thou relation which is brought into the light of the great synthesis. We thereby stand before the eternal Thou in whose omnipresence we all live. The centre of the suprapolar space is the personal God. The consequence of this for the problem of guilt is that the only guilt is guilt against the personal God. 'Against thee, thee only, have I sinned, and done this evil in thy sight.' We can sin against men and against things only because they are creatures of God. Responsibility is always responsibility to God. Conscience is always the consciousness that we are living under the all-seeing eye of God, and that we shall one day have to give account to Him of all that we have done and said.

20. SECULARISM OR THEISM

What we have had to say about natural law, the orders of creation and the problem of guilt has only confirmed and shed new light upon the general conclusion which we reached at the beginning of the last chapter, namely that we are confronted by an ultimate 'Either/Or' alternative upon which everything depends and which in the present situation of the world impinges on our consciousness more clearly than ever. Either the suprapolar space of God is an illusion, in which case there is no way out from the two states of mind, relativism and positivism, between which we are restlessly tossed to and fro in all fields of activity; or else the space of God is the omnipresent reality which comprises us together with all the rest of the world and in which everything finds repose and acquires an ultimate meaning.

At root, then, there are only two general conceptions of the world for us to choose between. All philosophies, nihilism, materialism, monism, mechanism, evolutionism, spiritualism, idealism and the rest, are always merely variants of one or other of these basic forms. The first of these two general conceptions is pure, consistent and mature secularism, which in all fields reckons only with relative values and finite quantities of energy. The other general conception is the belief in the living and personal God who governs all things. There can be no reconciliation between these two general conceptions. The struggle between them is even reflected in all philosophical and scientific theories of the universe and in all political and economic party programmes. All the forms of compromise which are repeatedly being devised in order to link these two conceptions of the universe are in the long run untenable and fall victims to their own lack of inner cohesion. Secularism, to be consistent, must necessarily attack the belief in the suprapolar space as being purely illusory. It must therefore entirely reject all such words as God, eternity, conscience, ethics, moral rearmament, guilt, responsibility, repentance, forgiveness and atonement, as inadmissible borrowings from a view of the world opposed to its own. It must strike them out of its vocabulary, as foreign bodies stemming from a different general picture of reality in which alone they possess a meaning. For as soon as even only one of these words is uttered, we find ourselves in the midst of the suprapolar space, so that all the relations in which we live and think are brought into a new light and all these fundamental words which pertain to the space of God come into force simultaneously all along the line.

If there are only these two underlying forms of thought and life, and if all the compromises which have been devised in order to combine them must, in the great conflict which is taking place today, be rejected from the very outset—such compromises, for example, as the notion of a 'non-religious morality' or the belief in a 'Deity' which remains an impersonal It, the 'Absolute' or the 'Unconditional'—then we find ourselves ultimately confronted by the one great question to which we are repeatedly led in every discussion between adherents of these two opposite views. Can a universally acceptable decision be reached between the two possibilities which are here in question? Or, more precisely, is there any means whereby one who with his whole thought and will lives in the polar space can be convinced of the existence of a second, suprapolar space?

If, as we have seen to be the case, secularism is not a logical or ethical principle but a space in which a man's whole existence may be confined as though within invisible prison walls, then obviously the secularists are in the same situation as the 'Flatlanders' in the story we have mentioned, who can see reality only in two dimensions. When there came on the scene beings who believed in a third dimension and asserted that they lived in a world in which three straight lines could intersect at right-angles, the Flatlanders were honestly convinced that people who made such assertions could only be visionaries who knew nothing of life and reality. They thought that all one could do was to lodge them in a lunatic asylum, since they were suffering from a morbid obsession. But if they were to disseminate their notion and thereby produce a mass delusion, they would have to be treated as a public danger and put under lock and key. This is in itself sufficient to explain why, in a nation in which the controlling authorities lived in the polar space, people who were grounded on theism could be treated as criminals and traitors.

This makes it all the more impossible to evade the question: Is there a means of persuading people who are confined within the endless prison of polar space that another space exists? Is there a key which I need only to put into the keyhole and turn, in order to open, for people from whom the suprapolar space is still hidden, the door which leads into this space? This question is usually expressed in the form: Is there a proof of the existence of God? Or, is there a proof that my ego is eternal, a proof of the immortality of the soul? But we have seen that the belief in a personal God who confronts me as a Thou and makes me His partner in conversation and so allows me to partake in His eternity, this belief can always arise only when a man is first of all caught up in the great nexus of the whole suprapolar region where all the relations in which we stand, including the I-Thou relation, move into the light of suprapolar thought. Consequently, we must always formulate the question as follows: Can the suprapolar space be disclosed to a being which has hitherto lived solely in the polar space? Can this be achieved by inferring from the world to its Originator, by an empirical proof or by a postulate?

Let us begin with the inference.[1] Bavink, in his *Natural Science on the Road to Religion*[2], made a particularly impressive attempt to demonstrate that, after the collapse of the mechanistic view of the universe, the destruction of the old

---

[1] cf. the general exposition of this question in *Naturwissenschaft und Religion (Natural Science and Religion)*, by Josef Engert, Meisenbach & Co., Bamberg, 1947.
[2] *Die Naturwissenschaft auf dem Weg zur Religion*, 1934.

concept of substance, and the undermining of the principle of causality by the statistical conception of natural laws, the 'hypothesis of God' is becoming indispensable for the explanation of the universe. Max Planck, too, showed in his work on natural science and religion that according to modern research the elementary component parts of the world structure are governed by a uniform plan. The course of nature proceeds in accordance with the 'principle of the minimum dissipation of energy'. Of all the conceivable processes, the real one is that for which the integral of a certain quantity, the so-called Lagrange function, with respect to time gives the minimum value. In this way the course of nature acquires a definitely teleological character. The achievement of a goal determines the development of the process. In this Max Planck sees evidence of the rule of a higher Reason, omnipotent over nature. A second fact must be added: on the basis of physical observations and measurements it is possible, by means of certain numbers and their mathematical derivatives, to reduce the so-called universal constants, among which Planck's efficiency quantum is of particular significance, and the prevailing functional relations between the elements, to regular mathematical formulas which enable us to make far-reaching predictions. The establishment of these constants rests upon the uniform results of all the relevant calculations. According to Planck this leads us to assume that a universal Mind stands behind the cosmos.

There can be no doubt that the conclusions reached by these two physicists fill anyone who already believes in God with reverence for the wonderful plan of the Creating Spirit whose footsteps we can everywhere trace in our study of nature. But the question which confronts us here is whether by any such inference from the wonderful design of the world a man whose thinking still lies outside the space of eternity can be convinced of the existence of a suprapolar space. The answer to this question must be no. We may indeed with a fair degree of probability draw from the construction of the world, so far as we can observe it, the conclusion that the Power which stands behind all this as a cause and which has designed this cosmic process in such a way that the purpose towards which the whole is directed is achieved in it with the relative minimum dissipation of energy—that this Power cannot be a mechanical cause, governing blindly. As Kant said, it is much more like a 'world architect'. We may compare it with a great technician and engineer, with a brilliant artist and organizer, who carries out with the least possible expenditure of material the design which he has in mind. But in drawing such a tremendously far-reaching inference as the inference from the world to a personal God, we must indeed proceed with the most scrupulous caution. We must not leave out any intermediate link in the argument. We must not advance a single step beyond what can be actually established. Even if we concede at once that the wonderful edifice of this world cannot be attributed to blind, mechanical forces, and that a thinking Power must stand behind it, conceiving a plan and executing it with the smallest possible expenditure of material, yet all the quantities of energy, the effects of which have been co-ordinated by this creating mind in accordance with a mathematically comprehensible plan, are still always energy factors of a limited energy quantum. Otherwise they could not be physically observed and measured at all. What we can infer exactly, then, is never more than an originator of the world which we can observe, one who disposes over finite and relative quantities of energy and distributes these in accordance with a plan which is conceived on a large scale.

No inferences from the wonderful design of the processes of nature can in any way enable us to determine whether the mind which is here creating is an *omnipotent* mind, of which it may be said 'With God nothing is impossible', or whether it has only limited power at its disposal and must work with limited supplies of energy, like all—even the greatest—technicians and artists of this world. And that is the question upon which everything depends. For between a mind which controls the masses of energy that are comprised in a galactic system and the *omnipotent* God there is still always an 'infinite qualitative difference'. In comparison with the omnipotent God, even the mighty mind which disposes over the forces of the galactic systems stands entirely on the same level as a human engineer who controls a great power station. In comparison with God even the greatest quantitative differences in this relative world sink into insignificance. Measured by the yardstick of God there is no difference at all between Mount Everest and an ant-hill. Consequently we *cannot* say that knowledge of the plan of the world process leads us to the hypothesis of 'God'. On the contrary, so long as the suprapolar space has still not been disclosed to us, none of these inferences from the contents of the polar world can bridge and pass beyond the infinitely deep gulf which divides the whole finite and relative world, the only possible object of the natural scientist's investigations, from the eternal God, who alone is absolute, unconditional and omnipotent. Not even the intelligent architect, the planning cosmic mind to which the contemporary view of nature repeatedly leads us, can be called God. Compared with God he is only a subordinate daemon with limited power and limited knowledge, a being, then, the worship of which would from the biblical point of view be idolatry. When we have ascertained the existence of this daemon, we cannot help going on to ask where it comes from and how it came into being. This can only lead us back to an anterior cause, and this in turn must have another cause, and so on *ad infinitum*.

But if no *causal inference* leads us out beyond the frontiers of the polar space, is there then perhaps an *empirical proof* whereby forces from the world beyond make themselves so clearly perceptible that it is no longer at all possible to deny the existence of a suprapolar space? This, too, would be possible if we were dealing, not with a space, but with a cosmos, forming, from the physical point of view, a 'closed system', and comprising an ascertainable energy quantum with a constant energy content. Only on this condition could it be shown that some particular occurrence, say the resuscitation of a dead man, cannot be explained by reference to the forces of this world and must arise from some supramundane source of energy. But in fact the totality of the polar cosmic space in which the secularist lives is not a closed system. Consequently, even the most incomprehensible occurrence, which looks like a violation of all the causal relations, can always be attributed to some intramundane force, which had hitherto remained unknown but which is easily able to counteract the effects of other forces. The experiences, too, of which we have already spoken, which the believer attributes to a higher dimension, the experience of an inner vocation or mission and the experience of guilt and pangs of conscience, are all indeed phenomena which, for him whose heart is pierced by them, are direct manifestations of God; yet, for him who sees them only objectively and from without, it is always possible to try to analyse them by the techniques of parapsychology or depth-psychology and to trace them back, for example, to that sub-conscious region of our soul-life, from which, especially in the case of those who, as James puts it, have a 'permeable margin of consciousness', there may come irruptions which produce such an extremely unsettling effect as to give rise to the notion that there is a supernatural world.

Max Hartmann, in his essay 'Atomic Physics, Biology and Religion',[1] has given an urgent warning, to those who are lay-men in the field of the natural sciences, against allowing them-selves to be led by the conclusions of contemporary atomic physics, in the form in which they have been laid before us by Pascual Jordan, into drawing theological inferences, particu-larly from the non-causal character of certain processes within the atom. In the light of what has been said, this warning is entirely justified. But we must go one step further than Hartmann goes in his essay, for we must warn theologians, especially, against drawing over-hasty inferences in which the wish is father to the thought. And we must in turn warn Hartmann himself against the danger which he has indicated. Even he has not entirely abstained from drawing the theo-logical consequences against which he cautions us; for he writes: 'The meaningfulness and the conformity to plan which are apparent in the laws of nature as a whole . . . may appear even to the critical scientist as an imposing revelation of God in nature.' In the light of all that has been said, this can be the case only if, quite independently of the impression which the meaningfulness and the planned regularity of the

[1] *Atomphysik, Biologie und Religion* in *Der Deutschenspiegel*, Stuttgart, 1947.

laws of nature make upon this 'critical scientist', there has been disclosed to him the space of eternity. So long as this space is still inaccessible to him, he may, as a critical scientist, just as well be led by the purely physical facts to accept the view which is nowadays maintained by the so-called Vienna circle, rejecting all inferences to transcendent realities and reducing the conclusions of modern physics to purely immanent forces.

If the suprapolar space can be reached neither by means of a causal inference nor by means of an empirical demonstration, there remains, according to Kant, only one other possible way of proving the existence of God. That is by making a *postulate*. A postulate does not, like a causal inference, start out from a fact which can be ascertained by observation, but from a practical attitude which we may adopt and on the basis of which we then have to put forward a definite *requirement* which must be fulfilled if the position we have taken up is to have a meaning. In Kant's case it was the recognition of the moral law, the requirements of which we, as autonomous beings, perceive in our conscience. This attitude, Kant says, leads to the 'belief of practical reason' that there stands behind the moral law an omnipotent Will which guarantees its realization. Another form of postulate is the path by which the physicist Gustave Mie is led to the belief in the personal God. Mie's position is particularly important for us in this connexion. He, too, does not set out from particular conclusions, reached in the course of his research in physics, such as might make possible a causal inference to a personal creator of the world, but from a practical attitude of belief which underlies all his investigations. According to Mie, all striving for scientific knowledge rests upon the belief 'that there is a truth and that we can know this truth if only we adopt the right attitude'. But, if it becomes clearly conscious, this belief in truth, and in our ability to know it, ends as belief in the veracious God. For, if it achieves complete clarity, it can be nothing other than the belief in a mind which is immanent in the entire cosmos, a mind in which the mind of every single individual is rooted.

This argument for theism is reminiscent of the postulate

upon which Descartes in his *Méditations,* a work which opens
a new epoch in the history of philosophy, based his proof of the
reality of the outer world.   The whole world which we see
around us might, in the nature of the case, be an illusion; for
our only immediate data are our own ego and the sensations
which this ego experiences.   According to Descartes, the
existence of a reality underlying these sensations ultimately
rests solely and exclusively on the fact that there is a God and
that this God is veracious and therefore unwilling to deceive
us, his creatures.   Yet, whether it sets out from the recognition
of a moral law or from belief in truth and the possibility of
attaining to it, no postulate of this kind can, in the light of
all that has so far been said, afford a proof of the existence of
the suprapolar space; for it is always a mere *petitio principii,*
an argument which begins by assuming as proved the very
thesis which it is intended to prove.   If we acknowledge in
our conscience a moral law which is unconditionally valid,
then we have already passed beyond the frontiers of the polar
space, in which there are always only relative values and
validities.   In other words, when we speak of the moral law,
we already find ourselves within the ambit of the eternal
archetypal space, in the centre of which stands the personal
God.   It is the same thing if we believe in a truth which is
unconditionally valid for all mankind.   This, too, means that
we have already found our way into the suprapolar space; for
within the polar world there can be no absolute truth, but
always only points of view, aspects of the world and attitudes
to it, all standing side by side on the same footing, and none
of them entitled to claim eternal validity.   Any postulate
from which we may set out is already a bridgehead which we
have won in the suprapolar space.   A postulate consists in
our advancing from one point which we have already secured
within the eternal space of God and taking possession of everything else which this space comprises.   But all that we have
done thereby is to render ourselves clearly conscious of that
which was vouchsafed to us from the beginning by virtue of
the disclosure of this space.

From this it follows that we have no means at our disposal
of breaking open the endless prison of the polar space and

gaining entrance to the suprapolar space. We can bring about
the discovery of the new space neither by a causal inference
from the world of experience nor by a postulate, neither by
thinking nor by an effort of the will.

It is to this negative fact that the Bible is referring when
it repeatedly states that only the 'temporal', i.e. the contents
of the polar space, 'is visible', but that 'the eternal', i.e.
the contents of the suprapolar space, 'is invisible' (τὰ γὰρ
βλεπόμενα πρόσκαιρα, τὰ δὲ μὴ βλεπόμενα αἰώνια, II Cor. 4.18).
God, therefore, who pertains to the space of eternity is
invisible. We cannot see Him unless we die, unless, that
is to say, we quit the whole space of visibility. The word
'see' does not refer here merely to the direct observation of
facts which are accessible to our organs of sense or which are
immediately disclosed to us through our insight into our own
ego (and this, as we have seen, is better known to us than the
whole external world). 'Seeing' also includes everything
which we can deduce from the contents of the polar space, so
apodeictically as to be able to win for it the credence of everyone else who stands, together with us, in this polar space.
That something should become accessible to us which lies outside the entire polar space, and pertains to the space of eternity, is possible only if there is a knowledge that is directed
towards something which can neither be seen nor inferred
from what has been seen. It must be a knowledge, then,
which, for anyone who has access only to the polar space,
appears totally inconceivable. For him it is quite incomprehensible that such a thing should even be possible.

This knowledge, the very possibility of which stands or falls
with the existence of a suprapolar space without which it is
unthinkable, is what the Bible calls 'faith'. The Epistle to
the Hebrews defines it as 'the evidence of things not
seen (πραγμάτων ἔλεγχος οὐ βγεπομένων, Heb. 11.1). Moses, we
are told in this chapter, 'endured as seeing him (God) who
is invisible' (τὸν γὰρ ἀόρατον ὡς ὁρῶν ἐκαρτέρησεν, Heb. 11.27).
This 'enduring' or holding fast to something, this being
held by something, resting upon something, something
which can neither be seen nor inferred from what is seen, but
something which is just as evidently real to us as any bodily

reality that we can see with our eyes and grasp with our hands—this was the underlying attitude in which all the men of the Bible lived their lives, their attitude from which they drew the strength to forsake everything and to take upon themselves torment and death for the sake of God. If we wish to express what the Bible calls 'faith' in the terminology of the present work, we must say that faith is the general condition in which we find ourselves if we are living completely consciously in the suprapolar space, with the same confidence and security with which the thoroughgoing secularist lives entirely in the polar space and regards as real only what confronts him in the form of this space, what, in other words, can be seen and touched and inferred from tangible facts. For any one who with all his thinking is held prisoner in the polar space, the entire psychological attitude which finds its expression in faith is totally incomprehensible. He too, indeed, recognizes invisible realities. These are the invisible causes which one may infer from their consequences, consequences which are themselves perfectly visible to us. One may infer, for example, from volcanic eruptions to an invisible subterranean fire, or from the vestigial hind-legs of whales to their extinct ancestors which appear to have lived on dry land. But all these invisible causes, precisely because we cannot see them but can only infer them, have the character of 'hypotheses'. However high a percentage of probability their reality may possess, it still always remains equally far removed from absolute, one-hundred-per-cent certainty.

Yet precisely this maximum of certainty is an essential characteristic of faith. Without it, faith cannot be that unshakable foundation of rock which withstands the onslaught of the entire visible world. 'I am persuaded,' says Paul, 'that neither death nor life . . . shall be able to separate us from the love of God' (Rom. 8.38f.). Seen from the standpoint of the polar space, the absolute certainty, which faith claims for itself here, can only be a dishonest attempt, by means of a sacrifice of the understanding, a *sacrificium intellectus,* or some theological sleight of hand, to misrepresent as a certainty that 'hypothesis of God' which after all, as should be honestly admitted, cannot possibly be proved and possesses therefore, at best, a very low percentage of probability. *Certainty* of faith, therefore, is conceivable only if, outside the polar space where there is no means of escape from this situation, there is some other omnipresent space, a space in which all the positive and negative inferences available to us within the polar space lose their validity. Certainty about something which nobody has ever seen can come only from the same source from which there came that 'eternal mission', that 'sacred necessity', in which the souls of the martyrs rested effortlessly while all the torments of their martyrdom passed over their bodies. It is only from the completely different dimension of the suprapolar space that there can arise this certainty which can be shaken by nothing that is of this world.

This renders all the more urgent the question of how the space of eternity, in which the believer lives, can become certainty for us, if it can be reached neither by means of empirical observation, nor by means of any kind of inference from ascertainable facts, nor yet by means of a postulate. There is only one answer to this question. If the space of eternity is to be discovered, there must first have taken place in the depths of our existence a transformation which is not within our control. We cannot ourselves bring about this all-transforming cataclysmic event, as we can bring about, for example, an electrical discharge by arranging an experiment; nor can we analyse and explain this event, as a doctor analyses and explains the process which has led to the curing of a disease. The event which must here occur stands entirely outside the domain over which we have control. All we can ever do is to speak afterwards, after the event has taken place, of an *occasion* which, in a particular instance, has given rise to this all-transforming occurrence in a man's life. But by this word 'occasion' we do not mean something like the 'immediate cause' which comes into operation in mechanical processes, setting them in motion by releasing a certain quantum of energy as the 'efficient cause'. An example of this 'immediate cause' would be the gentle push we give to the pendulum of a clock, bringing into play the mechanism which is driven by the fall of the weights. The 'occasion' of which we are

Q

speaking here is fundamentally different from an 'immediate cause' of this kind. For in the case of an 'immediate cause', such as the push received by the pendulum of the clock, we can predict with certainty that it will set the machine in motion. In the case of an 'occasion', in the sense in which we are here employing the word, the result is entirely incalculable. The same occurrence, which with one man in his present situation occasions the discovery of the eternal archetypal space, may with another man, or with the same man in another situation, pass by without leaving a trace.

Almost any occurrence, which disturbs us to the very depths of our being, may be the occasion whereby, in this unpredictable manner, the space of eternity is disclosed to us. It may be the death of one who is near to us which suddenly brings the eternal world very close. It may be a meeting with one who, as Bengel says, has the word 'Eternity' written on his forehead. It may be the shining eye of a child, which appears to us as a reflected gleam of light from a purer world from which this child comes. It may be a miraculous escape from death, such as thousands of people experienced during the war. Or else it may be some terrible catastrophe which has placed unforgettably before our eyes the transitoriness of all earthly things. It may be our finding ourselves in the condemned cell, where, as criminals under sentence of death, we are obliged to spend the last weeks of our lives. It may be a scientific discovery, which in a single night and at one stroke resolves a problem with which we had been tussling for years —falling now into our lap like a gift from heaven.. It may be the perception of a mathematical truth, as it was in the case of Pascal, who was led by the mystery of mathematical infinity directly to God. But for innumerable people in all the centuries of modern history the one great and completely decisive occasion, which brought about the transformation of their entire view of the world, was the encounter with the One who at a single stroke disclosed to them the space of God, which ever afterwards encompasses them on all sides like a field of force without which they can no longer live—the appearance of the person of Christ on earth and His journey to the Cross. Their experience was like that of the Russian,

Mereshkovski, who, after thirty years' reading of the Book which tells of Jesus, wrote in 1930 the words: 'I read it every day, and shall do so, so long as my eyes can see, by every light that comes from the sun and from the heart, on the brightest days and in the darkest nights, whether I be happy or unhappy, sick or in good health, believing or unbelieving, sensitive or insensitive. And it seems to me as if what I read is always something new, something unknown; as though I could never read all it has to tell and never know all the knowledge it can give. . . . You ask what I would wish to have laid beside me in my coffin? The Book. You ask what I would wish to have with me when I rise from my grave? The Book. What I have done on earth? I have read it. For men—perhaps for mankind—that is terribly much; but for the Book itself—it is terribly little.'

But we cannot ourselves bring about any of these great or small events which may occasion the discovery of the eternal archetypal space 'where and when God hath pleased', as the Reformers said, *ubi et quando visum est Deo*. To provoke such an event is not within our power. And if we are ourselves unable to bring about this crucial event, we are also unable ourselves to revoke and undo it when once it has come upon us, without any active intervention on our part. When once the space of the presence of God has been disclosed to us, beginning at the fateful hour in which this has occurred, it encompasses us so that we cannot escape from it. Our experience here may at first resemble that of a man who has escaped from a prison and who is standing again for the first time beneath the blue sky. He begins to praise and thank God for even his hardest and most incomprehensible experiences, even for a severe illness and the loss of all his possessions if these calamities have been the occasion of his discovering the space of God. But it is also possible that the discovery of the space of eternity which lies about us may produce a contrary effect. Thousands of our contemporaries are dimly conscious of the nearness of God, and yet such is the weight of the destiny they bear that they are no longer capable of thanking God for it. But because they still cannot escape from the impression that we are all standing in the presence of God, they begin to curse God and to wrangle with Him. It is with them as it was with the parson in Ernst Wiechert's novel *The Jeromin Children*. Because he could no longer bring the events of the world into harmony with his own existence, he regarded God as the great enemy whom he could never defeat though he struggled with Him till the hour of his death.

From this we see that if, without any active intervention on our own part and arising from some particular occasion which we have not ourselves brought about, the space of eternity has been disclosed to us, then we can no longer relapse into that secularism which has lost all understanding of the problem of God and which is quite indifferent to the struggle of faith. Our relation to God rather takes on the character of a Satanic rebellion. Even the Satanic pertains to the suprapolar space, as we shall see in a later context. Even the blasphemies we utter, the passionate questionings with which we assail God, are, if one may express it so, still always prayers, but prayers with a reversed sign.

The fact that the space of God cannot be disclosed either by proofs or by postulates, but that it is nevertheless an inescapable reality for him who has discovered it, might lead us to suppose that there are two separate groups of people, living in two distinct spaces and with no means of mutual comprehension remaining between them, and that we ought to abandon any attempt to initiate a discussion between them. We can only accept as an inescapable misfortune the fact that these two groups exist and that they cannot understand one another. We must confine our efforts to ensuring that their attitude to each other shall be one of mutual *tolerance*. If this were achieved, it would at last mean the end of that ancient struggle between belief and unbelief which has already wrought so much havoc in the history of the world. But even this way out is impracticable, although it seems to ease the situation enormously by putting an end to the whole conflict and burying the hatchet. Why can we not resign ourselves to an attitude of mutual toleration, which would at a single stroke call a halt to the impassioned struggle between the secularists and those who are still rooted in religion? This is impossible for the same reason which lay behind everything else we have discussed in this section. Tolerance is impracticable because the suprapolar region with which we are here concerned is a space which necessarily claims to comprise the whole of reality and to order the whole of reality in accordance with its own structural principle.

As soon as I have discovered this new space, I know from the very first moment that this space has not just come into being in the hour in which it has been disclosed to me. I know, on the contrary, that this space has always existed and that I have always been in it, but that I have been living in it like a blind man who gropes his way along with a stick, in the midst of a heavenly landscape which is suffused with radiant sunshine, because he does not see the space in which he is living. Yet I know, from the very moment at which my eyes are opened to a new space, not only that I myself was always encompassed by this space, although I had hitherto been unaware of it, but also that all my fellow-men, who are still stricken with blindness and who therefore regard me as a visionary, are themselves standing in this space, just as I am, but that their eyes are still closed. I know, indeed, that I have no power to open the eyes of other people to this space if it is still hidden from them. But I also know that all of them are now already standing in the midst of this space without being aware of it. I also know, when I myself have found peace in the space of God, that nobody who is still living in the polar space can ever come to rest in the two possibilities, relativism and positivism, between which, in that space, he is tossed endlessly to and fro.

Throughout the history of philosophy this idea has been expressed over and over again in various forms by men who, after finding peace in God, have looked back at their own past lives. Augustine says at the beginning of his *Confessions*: *cor nostrum inquietum est, donec requiescat in te.* This means that in all its intellectual and volitional activities our mind moves restlessly within infinite series, or else clings to something to which it must itself restlessly hold fast—until it finds peace in God. According to Pascal the self is a bottomless abyss (*abîme*) and I must fall uninterruptedly into its unplumbed depths without ever reaching the end. God alone can fill the abyss; in Him alone can this fall into the void be halted. So long as I have not found the firm ground 'which holds my anchor for ever', all I can do is to endure my restless condition, trying to become oblivious of myself through some intensive worldly occupation (*divertissement*), whether it be an intoxicating enjoyment of life or some great undertaking in public affairs which occupies all my thoughts by night and by day so intensely as to make me entirely forget my own ego. Kierkegaard in his *Sickness unto Death* says that everyone, however well it may go with him outwardly, goes on his way in a silent despair—even though he may still not be at all conscious of it—so long as he is intoxicated with life. Only God can heal this 'sickness unto death', if the man 'in faith transparently bases himself upon Him who placed him'.

It is because I have known all this since the very moment at which the space of God was disclosed to me, that there can never be peace between the two groups of people who live and think in the two opposite forms of existence, secularism and theism. It is therefore impossible to remain neutral with regard to the ultimate crucial question which confronts us all and to recognize these two attitudes as being equally legitimate. The secularist must necessarily passionately oppose as a dangerous illusion the entire belief in a space of the presence of God, together with all the ethical consequences which are derived from it. Bleuler, looking at it from his materialist point of view and as a doctor, once described the whole complex of *idées fixes* pertaining to the suprapolar region as 'dereism', thus classifying it pathologically as a symptom of a disease of the brain which must be combated by every possible means. And, like the secularist, the man who is rooted in God is also unable to acknowledge the legitimacy of the other form of existence. Face to face with this other form of existence he cannot withdraw into an attitude of silent tolerance and understanding sympathy. For he knows that, as we have seen, whatever occurs in this world, including any encounter with a human being, may be the 'occasion' which perhaps will bring about the great all-transforming discovery in a man's life. Because this possibility is always present, even though I never have control over it, it must be the most intense desire of every believer that he may act and speak and write in such a way that his whole existence, both active and passive, may be for those around him the 'occasion' which brings about the great event, the discovery of the space of God, even for those from whom this space was hitherto concealed. It was from this point of view that Paul wrote of his whole life: 'I am *debtor* both to the Greeks, and to the Barbarians; both to the educated and the uneducated' (Rom. 1.14), and that Peter and John replied to the Sanhedrin, when it was trying to forbid them to speak in public: 'We cannot but speak the things which we have seen and heard' (Acts 4.20).

We are confronted here by the ultimate enigma inherent in the reality in which we find ourselves. If we attempt to formulate this reality in terms of a philosophy we are faced, as we have seen, with a conflict between two possibilities which cannot be reconciled. The first possibility is the general outlook of secularism, that with which we all find ourselves at birth. This is the world picture of the polar space which encompasses us on all sides. The second possibility is the world-picture of faith, a picture in which the personal God forms the supreme centre, in accordance with Cusanus's saying that 'God is a circle of which the centre is everywhere and the circumference nowhere'. We are not born into this second overall view of the world; it can only fall into our laps by means of a 'second birth', as a gift which we cannot ourselves procure but which, when it has been apportioned to us, we also cannot ourselves revoke. The conflict between these two general conceptions, from which there also always result two contrary views of nature, is the deepest root of all the tensions in which we live, including all the ideological struggles which affect even political and economic life. This conflict is always present, and it provokes a struggle which keeps the world in a state of permanent upheaval and cannot be brought to a standstill by means of mutual tolerance. This conflict is the underlying feature of the world-form in which we are now living. It is evidence of the fact that the whole of reality is in a state of unresolved tension. We are, indeed, conscious of the abnormality of the whole state of the world only if we are believers. The unbeliever is only dimly aware of it. For we stand in two spaces at once, spaces with contrasting structures. The one space is the space into which we have been born, together with all other beings. In this space we live and think and explore in accordance with the generally accepted methods of natural science together with all the others. We can communicate with all thinking beings in a way which ensures mutual comprehension and general agreement. The second space is that which is disclosed to us only by a 'second birth', as it were by a 'second sight'. With regard to this second space we can communicate only with those who have undergone the same experience as ourselves. Even we ourselves can live in this second space only by ever anew wielding the 'nevertheless of faith' to combat whatever comes against us from the polar space and tries to cast doubt upon the reality of the suprapolar space. This cleavage, which runs right through the whole state of the world, does not merely prevent the ending of the ideological struggle between the secularists and those who are rooted in religion; it passes also through the soul of the believer himself as a daily temptation to forsake his faith.

These considerations have prompted the idea that the whole of reality in its present form is not in its normal state, that is to say it is no longer in its original state and not yet in its definitive state but in an *unresolved* intermediate state which bears the character of a 'Paradise Lost' and is directed towards a consummation in which those riddles will be solved which in the present form of reality remain insoluble. That is the underlying thought from which the New Testament sets out and to which it repeatedly reverts. When it concerns itself with the resolving of this disharmony which runs through the whole world, it does not speak merely of the destiny of men and of the history of mankind, which form only a small segment of the whole of reality. Paul's assertions always include the whole of nature, when he says: 'The . . . *whole* creation ($\pi \hat{a} \sigma a$ $\dot{\eta}$ $\kappa \tau \acute{\iota} \sigma \iota s$) groaneth *with us* and travaileth in pain together until now.' 'The creature was made subject to vanity.' 'The creature shall be delivered from the bondage of corruption' (Rom. 8). We cannot grasp the whole profound meaning of these universal assertions, which embrace the entire cosmos, until we have first considered the view of the universe which is presented by modern physics, biology and astronomy, together with all that can be scientifically ascertained with regard to the origin and end of the world. Only then can we at least dimly understand how the disharmony between the two conceptions of the universe, that of secularism and that of faith, the disharmony from which our intramundane thinking sees no way of escape, finds a solution which comes from God. To demonstrate this will be the purpose of the remaining parts of this work.

INDEXES

INDEX OF NAMES

253

INDEX OF SUBJECTS